Relapse Prevention Therapy Workbook

Identifying Early Warning Signs

Related to Personality and Lifestyle Problems

Updated, Revised, and Simplified

By Terence T. Gorski and Stephen F. Grinstead

Based on the GORSKI-CENAPS® Model

Produced by The CENAPS Corporation
13194 Spring Hill Drive
Spring Hill, FL 34609
Phone: (352) 596-8000
Fax: (352) 596-8002
E-mail: *info@cenaps.com*

Herald Publishing House/Independence Press
1001 West Walnut St.
Independence, MO 64050
Phone: 1-800-767-8181 or (816) 521-3015
Fax: (816) 521-3066
Website: *www.relapse.org*

Printed in the United States of America
ISBN: 978-0-8309-1487-6

For additional copies of this book, please contact Herald Publishing House/Independence Press at 1-800-767-8181 or (816) 521-3015 or go to *www.relapse.org* to place an order.

Training Contact
For training information contact: (352) 596-8000 or e-mail *info@cenaps.com*.

Table of Contents

Terry's Introduction

I have been working on the development of Relapse Prevention Therapy since 1972. The development has been long and hard because I have done all research and development on my own time while using my own personal resources. Fortunately, the various published versions of the workbook have been well-received. As a result the royalties and the donation of time and effort by many people over the years have been sufficient to finance its ongoing development.

In this version of the RPT workbook our goal was to make the book more user-friendly by simplifying the exercises, reducing the number of exercises, and providing real examples of how clients who succeeded with RPT completed some key exercises.

I hope this version of the workbook will be useful and effective in helping you find long-term recovery. Recovery from addiction is hard. There is no easy way out. But these exercises may prove helpful. Many people have benefited from the completion of the RPT workbook. But some have not. If you find this workbook is too complicated, you can start the Relapse Prevention Process by getting the *Relapse Prevention Counseling (RPC) Workbook* (*www.relapse.org*), which focuses on identifying and managing high-risk situations.

I wish you well on your journey to find a meaningful and comfortable life in recovery.

—Terence T. Gorski

Steve's Introduction

I've been working with Terry Gorski's CENAPS® model since 1986. My supervisor, Molly Burke, from an inpatient addiction-treatment program, was one of the first clinicians to become an advanced certified relapse prevention specialist through the Gorski-CENAPS® Relapse Prevention Therapy School. At the time, I was the primary therapist for that program's Addiction Pain Treatment track. I discovered the information she was bringing back was making a big difference with my addicted pain patients.

I used the Gorski-CENAPS® model with pain patients in that program until I went to Chicago in 1991 to become certified myself. I had been in my own recovery almost 10 years and had been working in the field of addiction about eight years. I thought this relapse prevention training would be useful. Wow! What an understatement!

I am so grateful I decided to take this training. What I learned changed not only my professional life but saved me from a potential relapse in my own recovery. At this training, the students have to put themselves in the role of a relapse client and work through all the experiential exercises you will be asked to complete in this workbook. Instead of creating a fictitious role-play client, I decided, like many others also do, to use my own recovery. I'm very glad I did.

I went on to complete the competency certification and was invited to join Terry's Relapse Prevention Therapy School faculty. I have taken more than a thousand relapse clients through the original course—a combination of the *Staying Sober Workbook,* the *Relapse Prevention Therapy Workbook,* the *Relapse Prevention Counseling Workbook,* and the *Addiction-Free Pain Management Relapse Prevention Workbook*. I have seen the remarkable difference this strategic process can make in people's lives.

I have been co-teaching the five-day Relapse Prevention Therapy School with Terry since 1996. For several years we have been modifying the process and field testing all the exercises you will be working through in this newly revised *Relapse Prevention Therapy Workbook*.

If you are willing to be open and honest and complete each developmental exercise in this new workbook, you may never have to experience the pain of relapse again. We have worked very hard to boil this down to 14 strategic exercises that will help you identify and manage your personal self-defeating pattern of warning signs that set you up to relapse.

—Stephen F. Grinstead

How to Get the Most from this Workbook

The *Relapse Prevention Workbook* is designed for people in recovery from alcohol or other drug addiction who have a history of relapse, or are afraid they might relapse. Confusion and misunderstanding continue to exist about what relapse is and how it happens. We want to clarify our definition of relapse, how it happens, and most importantly how to prevent you from entering the relapse cycle.

What Does the Term ***Relapse*** Really Mean?

If you ask people in recovery from an addictive disorder about relapse they probably will say relapse is going back to using alcohol or other drugs. Another common definition is that a person goes back to the addiction process. While that definition is partially correct, the full explanation of relapse is much more complex.

What many people don't realize is that the chemical use is not the beginning of a relapse. It is the final step in an ongoing *relapse process*. In addition, relapse is a common symptom of chemical dependency, and one-third to two-thirds of all recovering alcoholics/addicts relapse despite their best intentions not to do so.

If someone also is living with a coexisting disorder—e.g., depression—the instance of relapse can be even higher because these other problems easily can become a relapse justification. Fortunately, the rate of relapse can be lowered if recovering people are exposed to education and training about relapse prevention and how to deal more effectively with coexisting problems. Prevention is much easier than crisis management.

We believe relapse education must start with a new definition of relapse. The definition we propose: ***Relapse is the process of becoming dysfunctional in recovery. Relapse is a progressive series of events that takes people from a stable recovery through various stages of dysfunction and eventually back to using alcohol or their other drug of choice.***

Relapse is the process
of becoming dysfunctional in recovery.

When you start on the slide to relapse you undergo many changes. One of the first changes is a return to denial that at first has nothing to do with substance use. In other words, you begin denying you need to work a program of responsible living, healthy communication with others, and constantly looking at yourself for evidence of progress and problems in your life. To deny these needs leads to thinking problems.

Now instead of responsible recovery-prone positive thinking you start experiencing relapse-prone negative thinking and even euphoric recall. Euphoric recall is remembering how good the alcohol or other drugs used to work and how awful it is that you can't use them now.

This negative thinking leads to experiencing uncomfortable and/or painful emotions. These feelings produce self-defeating urges often followed by self-destructive behaviors. Inappropriate use of alcohol or other drugs may not be an option in the early stages of relapse, but the negative behaviors often set you up to experience even more problems.

Being in recovery demands learning new tools. You need to move from an addiction-centered lifestyle to a recovery-centered one. In the same way, when you are trying to remain in recovery you need to learn all you can about the sobriety-based symptoms of an addictive disorder and to develop new tools for coping with them.

The other important task for relapse-prone people is to be able to identify and manage their patterns of self-defeating thoughts and behaviors that we call ***relapse warning signs***. You are beginning an exciting—and possibly frightening—journey of self-discovery. Hold on tight, and hang in there because the journey is worth it.

Part A: Your Workbook Roadmap

Below are the exercises that this workbook leads you through.

Exercise One—Stress Self-Monitoring: *Self-monitoring* is one of the most-effective techniques in cognitive behavioral therapy. Research shows that by self-monitoring any behavior we want to change, the behavior usually begins to change in a positive direction. The term *self-monitoring* simply means paying attention to specific thoughts, feelings, urges, actions, and social reactions. In this exercise you will learn to do stress monitoring using the stress thermometer. The stress thermometer is an easy-to-use tool for identifying your stress level and deciding if you need to take action to lower your stress before continuing with the RPT Process.

Exercise Two—Learning from Past Efforts at Recovery: In this exercise you learn about the three criteria necessary to be a good candidate for the Relapse Prevention Therapy process. You do this by exploring the strengths and weaknesses of previous attempts at recovery. You also learn to identify *Hidden Warning Signs* that easily can be overlooked or ignored. You also learn about using the warning sign cards that you can find in the Appendix section of this book. You start developing your *First Stack of Warning Sign Cards* at this point. In this exercise we will be working only with *Titles* and *Descriptions* from side one of the warning sign cards.

Exercise Three—Life and Addiction History: In this exercise we will ask you to look at each stage of your life in a way that will help you identify the important patterns or cycles of events more clearly. The purpose of completing *The Life and Addiction History* is to identify *the pattern of recurring life problems* that sets you up to relapse. You will develop your *Second Stack of Warning Sign Cards* at this point. You will focus on looking for any *Hidden Warning Signs in the Life and Addiction History.* We will lead you through a strategic process, and by the end of this exercise you will have developed many more warning sign cards to add to your deck.

Exercise Four—Recovery and Relapse Calendar: In this exercise you will learn to build your personal relapse calendar. The calendar helps you remember how many relapse episodes you've had, what started them, and how long they lasted. A relapse episode is a period when you used alcohol or drugs that was followed by at least 10 days of abstinence. You then develop a *Relapse Episode List* designed to help you notice what happened when you tried not to use alcohol and drugs in the past. By understanding what happened during these times, you can see what to change. You are asked to refer to your relapse calendar while you do this exercise. You end this exercise by developing your *Third Stack of Warning Sign Cards* by reviewing the summary of the recovery and relapse history while looking at *The Recovery and Relapse History—Hidden Warning Signs.* We again lead you through a strategic process, and by the end of this exercise you will have developed even more warning sign cards to add to your deck.

Exercise Five—Review of the Warning Sign List: In this exercise you are asked to read aloud and explore the 15 common warning signs that lead from stable recovery to relapse. You then are asked to review the warning signs on the *Warning Sign List.* Next, select three warning signs that apply to you. Answer specific questions about each and develop your *Initial Warning Sign List.* Then review the answers to each question you answered for all three warning signs from your initial warning sign list. We then help you develop your *Fourth Stack of Warning Sign Cards* to add to your deck. Finally you combine all of your card stacks. We guide you through a strategic, step-by-step process with the result having a sequence of warning sign cards in the order that the warning signs generally happen.

Exercise Six—Developing Your Final Warning Sign Card Sequence: In this exercise you learn that one warning sign causes the next one to occur. The first warning sign happens, and then we think self-defeating thoughts that cause us to have unmanageable feelings, which create the urge to act out the next warning sign. The result is a tight sequence of warning sign cards that shows how your relapse sequence could happen.

Exercise Seven—Identifying Three Critical Warning Signs (CWS): In this exercise you select three (3) key or *Critical-Warning Signs.* These signs can alert you to the fact that you're moving toward relapse and give you a chance to stop the process before it gets too strong.

Exercise Eight—TFUAR Analysis: Managing Thoughts: In this exercise you learn to analyze your *Critical Warning Signs* by understanding the thoughts, feelings, urges, actions, and reactions (TFUARs) related to managing the warning signs in a way that leads to becoming dysfunctional in recovery or even relapsing. In this exercise you also start the TFUAR process with the thoughts section for your three *Critical-Warning Signs*.

Exercise Nine—TFUAR Analysis: Managing Feelings: In this exercise you are introduced to a feeling checklist and feeling-management skills to complete the TFUAR process with the feelings section for your three *Critical-Warning Signs*.

Exercise Ten—TFUAR Analysis: Managing Urges: In this exercise you are guided through a process of identifying and managing the self-defeating urges that set you up for relapse with your three *Critical-Warning Signs*.

Exercise Eleven—TFUAR Analysis: Managing Actions: In this exercise you are guided through a process of identifying and managing the self-destructive actions or behaviors that set you up for relapse with your three *Critical-Warning Signs*.

Exercise Twelve—TFUAR Analysis: Managing Personal Reactions: In this exercise you learn to tie together everything you have learned from completing the previous four exercises with your three *Critical-Warning Signs*.

Exercise Thirteen—Building a Recovery Program for Relapse Prevention: In this exercise you see that you have identified and learned to manage the Critical-Warning Signs that lead from stable recovery to relapse. Next it is time to develop a schedule of recovery activities that can help you identify and manage those *Critical-Warning Signs*.

Exercise Fourteen—Building Your Relapse Prevention Recovery Plan: In this exercise you learn to develop an initial recovery plan by (1) entering the day and time of scheduled recovery activities (it is helpful to have two or three activities scheduled each day); (2) describing the recovery activity; and (3) describing the primary goal of that activity in preventing relapse. You then construct a final recovery plan that addresses the weaknesses you discovered in your initial recovery plan by systematically comparing it to your warning sign list. You do this by: (1) entering time of scheduled recovery activities for each day; (2) describing each recovery activity; and (3) describing the primary goal of that activity in preventing relapse. Then you will end the book by learning to complete the Morning and Evening Inventories exercise.

Part B: Introducing Relapse Warning Signs

Relapse warning signs are the experiences recovering people have that create unnecessary pain, problems, and cravings (urges to use alcohol and other drugs), setting them up to reactivate their addiction despite their previous commitment not to. It helps to know the general progression of relapse warning signs from the beginning of the Relapse Prevention Process. Please review the *Relapse Warning Sign Elements* and the *Relapse Cycle.* Then discuss them with your therapist or relapse prevention coach.

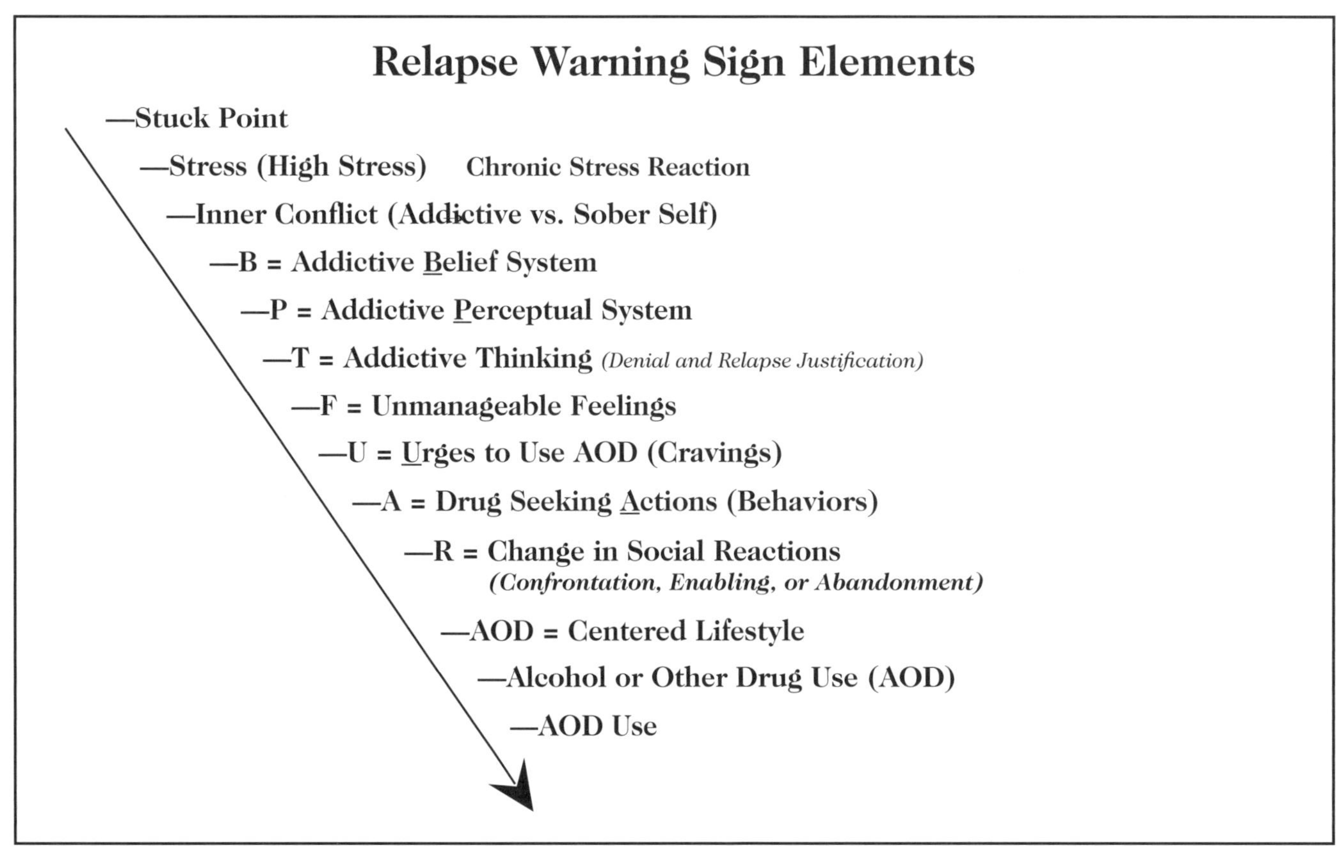

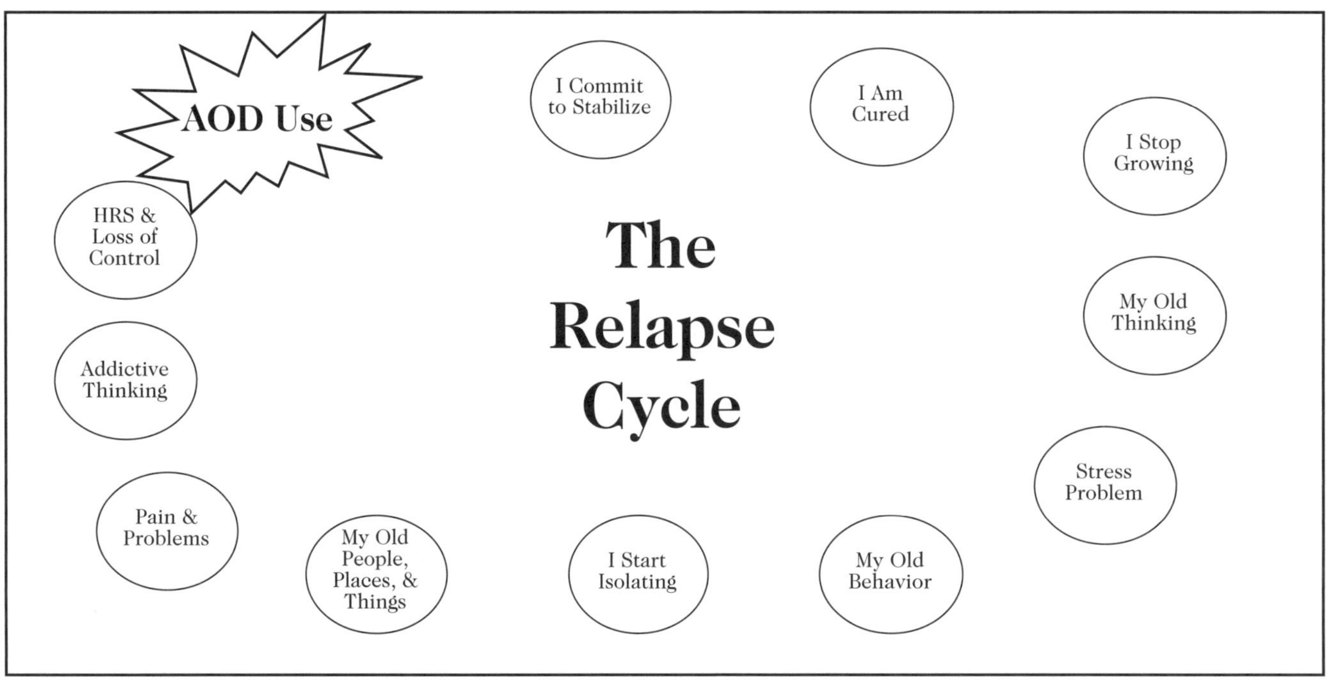

Part C: Introducing Jill and Phil

In the course of developing this workbook we used two client examples that are a composite of several actual clients. We changed their names and some information for confidentiality reasons. We use their experiences with completing the Relapse Prevention Warning Sign Process to give you concrete examples of how to correctly complete some of the most-important and most-difficult exercises.

Our goal in giving these examples is to show you how this process works with real relapse people in the real world. We do not give examples for every exercise because many of these exercises are simple, straightforward, and easy to understand. We selected the most-important exercises that our experience has shown give recovering people the most-important problems in working the relapse prevention process. These examples should help you see how the Relapse Prevention Warning Sign Process works.

With that in mind, we want you to meet the two people who will help you by giving examples from their own relapse prevention work. We named them Jill and Phil.

Introducing Jill

Jill is a 35-year-old married woman, mother of a teenage son by a previous marriage and two daughters under five. She is living with her second husband. Jill's teenage son is actively chemically dependent, and her spouse is physically, verbally, and emotionally abusive. As a result she lives in stressful conditions that interfere with her ability to stay sober by increasing the likelihood of her using alcohol or other drugs to get emotional relief from the difficult circumstances of her life.

Jill is obsessive (i.e., she tends to keep thinking about something over and over again) and compulsive (once she starts doing something she keeps doing it and has a hard time stopping). She tends to act out by using repetitive behaviors that have little or nothing to do with helping to solve the immediate problems she faces. As a result, a central focus of treatment is to help her pause when facing a problem and select a relevant response to help solve the problem, rather than acting out repetitive, self-defeating patterns of behavior.

Jill's father suffers from prescription-drug dependency and often encourages her to take addictive medications. Jill has an extremely difficult time with trust and is very resistant to opening up in self-help groups. This is compounded by the fact that her first husband also abused her and her son.

Jill has a long history of alcohol and opiate addiction with three treatment episodes and two substance-related arrests. She started drinking as a young teen and was drinking alcoholically by her senior year of high school. While in college she started using other drugs but always favored alcohol. This changed when she started mixing her father's prescription opiates with her drinking in her mid-20s. This resulted in her first DUI and first serious treatment episode.

Jill experienced her first of three relapse episodes three months after successfully completing her first treatment program. Jill voluntarily enrolled in an outpatient addiction-treatment program and this time stayed sober almost three years. Jill blamed her second relapse on being physically abused by her husband, and she drank to cope with the emotional pain. This time she sought help from a local battered-women's shelter. Her counselor was a recovering alcoholic who helped her get back into her recovery.

Jill's second legal problem was another arrest for her second DUI charge, which ended her most-recent relapse episode. This time Jill was drinking and again had mixed some of her father's prescription pain pills. This brought her to Dr. Grinstead's practice for relapse prevention therapy.

It is crucial to discover your own motivation for treatment and build on it.

Jill's motivation for relapse prevention treatment came as a result of her DUI plus the shame and guilt she experienced from her relapse after being sober for five years this time.

Introducing Phil

Phil is a 50-year-old divorced male who has a long history of addictive disorders and has been in more than 10 addiction treatment programs over the last 15 years. He was able to remain clean and sober as long as two years at one point. Phil also has several relationship problems. Most critical was a very emotional relationship that ended a long-term relationship. He was engaged, and his fiancée also was in recovery. Phil relapsed for the third time in less than a year when she got scared about relapsing and felt she needed to end the relationship to save her sobriety. One day she suddenly ended the engagement and moved out. Phil didn't see it coming. He felt rejected and hurt. He believed he couldn't deal with the pain while sober. He began using alcohol and opiates to try to manage the pain and solve his relationship problems.

Phil started drinking when he was 10 years old. His parents were alcoholics, and he was raised by his mother. She was raised in an addictive family with a series of abusive, alcoholic stepfathers. Phil's father was not a very big part of his life and rarely saw Phil when Phil was growing up.

Phil was drinking alcoholically by his sophomore year in high school. He had found marijuana and heroin by his senior year, but alcohol remained his drug of choice. In his mid-30s, Phil found speed—both illicit methamphetamine and prescription Dexedrine. He reported that the speed allowed him to drink even more alcohol.

Addicted people often become socially isolated.

Phil has a tendency to isolate when experiencing emotion or pain. After his initial chemical relapse, he was unable to open up and be honest at his self-help meetings or with his sponsor. After meetings he often found himself at bars, where he found it easy to persuade himself he deserved relief. He always looked for others with worse drinking problems than his to convince himself that he didn't really have a problem.

He finally admitted to his current sponsor and to himself that he was really out of control and just wanted to drink and use opiates to help him cope with his uncomfortable feelings and to find a feeling of euphoria. He admitted this would help him to escape and forget about his problems for a little while. Phil also suffered from extreme shame about past sexual trauma that caused sexual dysfunction, which he believes led to his divorce and was a problem in his recently ended intimate relationship. He finally was ready to get help.

Phil's principal motivation for treatment was the result of his engagement ending after his latest relapse. His partner told him she would not even reconsider discussing getting back together unless he underwent and succeeded with relapse prevention therapy. She also said he needed to be willing to go into couples therapy after finishing his relapse prevention therapy.

Part D: Let the Journey of Discovery Begin

By completing the exercises in this workbook you will begin a journey of self-discovery and personal change. Trust the process. Get someone to help you review each exercise and give you feedback about your answers. This is best done by a therapist who also is certified as a relapse prevention specialist. You can find a list of certified relapse prevention specialists at *www.cenaps.com*.

This workbook is designed to help you learn to identify and manage patterns of self-defeating behaviors that probably started in childhood. This process of self-discovery takes a considerable amount of courage and perseverance. To be successful you need to be willing to put in the time and effort. If you are diligent, the rewards are worth it.

Please go to the next page to begin your relapse prevention journey of discovery and learn about stress self-monitoring.

Exercise No. 1: Stress Self-Monitoring

Self-monitoring is one of the most-effective techniques used in cognitive behavioral therapy. Research has shown that by self-monitoring any behavior we want to change, the behavior usually begins to change in a positive direction.

The term *self-monitoring* simply means to pay attention to a specific thought, feeling, behavior, or social interaction. This is done by:

1. *Anticipating* experiences that could tempt you to use the old, self-defeating or addictive behavior;
2. *Preparing* to use alternative behavior as a substitute for the self-defeating behavior;
3. *Staying in the moment* as you use the new behavior by consciously noticing how well the substitute behavior is working and if you are tempted to or actually start using the old behavior;
4. *Debriefing* when the situation is over by taking time to evaluate how things went and making plans to do things a little better if similar situations arise in the future

Stress Management is a critical component in *Relapse Prevention Therapy (RPT)*. The lower your stress while completing and discussing each exercise, the easier it will be to complete that exercise, and the more you will learn. To help you effectively monitor your stress levels we suggest you use ***The Stress Thermometer*** provided below. The stress thermometer is an easy-to-use tool for identifying your stress level and deciding if you need to take action to lower your stress before continuing with the RPT process.

Exercise 1—Part A: The Stress Thermometer

	20	Psychosis/Collapse
Trauma Reaction	15	Dissociation
	10	Loss of Control
	9	Overreact
Stress Reaction	8	Driven/Defensive
	7	Loss of Focus—Space Out
	6	Free Flow with Effort
Functional Stress	5	Free Flow with No Effort
	4	Focused & Active
	3	Relaxed—Focused
Relaxation	2	Relaxed—Not Focused
	1	Relaxed—Nearly Asleep

Keeping Stress Low while Thinking and Talking about Upsetting Things

The goal is to keep your stress level in the functional zone (between 4 and 6). ***If your stress drops below a 4,*** your mind will wander, and you won't be able to stay focused or put enough energy into completing the exercise. If your stress level gets to a 6 or above (6, 7, 8, 9, 10, 10+) you will tend to lose focus and get driven and defensive. The higher your stress goes the more problems you will experience. When your stress level reaches a level 9 or higher you easily can start to use automatic ***survival defenses,*** such as fighting (getting angry, belligerent, or violent), fleeing (mentally checking-out of the session or leaving treatment against advice), or freezing (becoming compliant and saying or doing anything you think the therapist or coach wants you to say to get them to leave you alone).

To be able to benefit from RPT or any other form of therapy, counseling or coaching you must learn to recognize when your stress rises above a level 7 and learn relaxation techniques that you can use to lower your stress below a level 7.

Exercise 1—Part B: Techniques for Lowering Stress

1. **Deep Breathing:** Take a deep breath, hold it for a moment, and slowly exhale. (Repeat three times.)
2. **Change Body Posture:** Put your feet flat on the floor, push your buttocks back in the chair, sit straight, and gently stretch your head up toward the ceiling.
3. **Body Check:** Start with your feet and notice any feelings or sensations in your feet. Imagine a warm, tingling sense of relaxation in your feet. (Repeat with lower legs, upper legs, lower back, stomach, upper back, neck, shoulders, upper arms, lower arms, and hand and fingers.)
4. **Muscle Tensing and Release:** Focus on each group of major muscles and ask the person to tense them as tightly as possible and hold for the count of three. Then totally release the tension and notice the sense of relaxation that comes into the muscle. Use the words "release and relax" to condition the relaxation response.
5. **Guided Imagery:** Imagine you are in a safe, peaceful, and relaxing place. Notice what you see, hear, feel, touch, taste, and smell. Allow yourself to feel safe, comfortable, and relaxed as you create this image.
6. **Hypnotic Counting:** Counting backward from 10 to zero. After each number, say to yourself, "deeper and deeper relaxed." For example: 10, deeper and deeper relaxed. 9, deeper and deeper relaxed, etc.
7. **Singing the Vowel Sounds:** In your mind, sing the vowel sounds (A, E, I, O, U).
8. **Gratitude List:** Create a list of good things happening in your life. Memorize it. Constantly review it. When you notice your stress is going up and you are using negative thinking, get into positive thinking.
9. **Detach and Choose to Relax:** Use the following affirmations: (1) What is—is! (2) I am not what is! (3) I can choose how I respond to what is! (4) I can choose to lock onto what is, identify with it, and get stressed out! (5) I can choose to detach from what is, relax, seek help, respond to what I have the power to change, and let go of or turn over that which I have no power to change.
10. **Prayer and Reflection:** Select a soothing prayer to the God of your understanding. Memorize it and repeat it slowly in your mind, reflecting on the meaning of the prayer and how it applies to you in the moment.

Exercise 1—Part C: Relaxation Training

You can train yourself to increase your ability to relax by picking one or more of the above stress-reduction tips and then completing the following exercise:

1. Sit in a quiet place, where you won't be disturbed.
2. Rate your **current stress level**, and write it on a sheet of paper.
(current stress level = ___)
3. Take one minute by the clock, ***raise*** your stress level as high as you can for one minute, rate your stress level, and write it down.
(high stress level = ___)
4. Remember to write down what you did in your mind and body to raise your stress level.
5. Take one minute by the clock, ***lower*** your stress level as far as you can, rate your stress level, and write it down.
(low stress level = ___)
6. Write the relaxation techniques that you used to lower your stress.

Ongoing Practice

1. Practice the above exercise four times per day (breakfast, lunch, dinner, and before bed), noting your stress level before and after.
2. Whenever you think of it during the day, notice and rate your stress level. Write it on a card with the time and why you rated the stress as you did.

This excercise ends here.

Exercise No. 2: Learning from Past Efforts at Recovery

Exercise 2—Part A: Criteria for Relapse Prevention Warning Sign Management

Criteria No. 1: Previously Completed a Primary Addiction-Recovery Process:

1. Have you completed a primary treatment/recovery process for addiction to alcohol or other drugs? (This may be a professional inpatient or a professional outpatient program.) Did this program include:

   A. An education program that explained addiction, recovery, relapse, and ongoing community recovery resources? ❑ Yes ❑ No Please explain.

   ____

   ____

   B. Did you attend twelve-step meetings during the program? ❑ Yes ❑ No

   ____

   ____

   C. Did you complete the program? ❑ Yes ❑ No Please explain:

   ____

   ____

   D. Did you leave the program convinced you were addicted to alcohol or other drugs? ❑ Yes ❑ No Please explain:

   ____

   ____

   E. Did you leave the program committed to participate in an ongoing recovery program? ❑ Yes ❑ No

   Please describe the recovery program:______________________________

   ____

   ____

2. During your previous periods of recovery did you actively participate in a personal recovery program?

   ❑ Fully ❑ Partially ❑ Not at all Please explain:

   ____

   ____

3. During your previous periods of recovery did you actively work a twelve-step recovery program?

   A. Did you have a home group? ❑ Yes ❑ No Please explain:

   ____

   ____

B. Did you have a sponsor? ❑ Yes ❑ No Please explain:

C. Did you work the steps? Which steps did you work?
❑ Yes ❑ No Please explain:

4. During your previous periods of recovery did you…

A. Develop an accurate understanding of addiction?
❑ Fully ❑ Partially ❑ Not at all Please explain:

B. Recognize that you were addicted?
❑ Fully ❑ Partially ❑ Not at all Please explain:

C. Develop a commitment to stop using alcohol and other drugs and work an abstinence-based recovery program?
❑ Fully ❑ Partially ❑ Not at all Please explain:

5. During your past periods of recovery did you…

A. Stabilize from acute withdrawal?
❑ Fully ❑ Partially ❑ Not at all Please explain:

B. Stabilize from severe post-acute withdrawal (i.e. become able to think clearly, manage your emotions, remember things, sleep restfully, and manage stress without shutting down or overreacting)?
❑ Fully ❑ Partially ❑ Not at all Please explain:

C. Learn to manage or stop having cravings to use.

❑ Fully ❑ Partially ❑ Not at all Please explain:

____

____

(Note: To accomplish these three things usually means staying abstinent and working a recovery program for 90 days or longer.)

6. **Hidden Relapse Warning Signs:** In reviewing the above information did you notice anything that has or may have contributed to a relapse? ❑ Yes ❑ No

Please list the three most important things you noticed that may have contributed to your relapse.

A. The first thing I noticed that may have contributed to relapse was…

____

____

B. The second thing I noticed that may have contributed to relapse was…

____

____

C. The third thing I noticed that may have contributed to relapse was…

____

____

Criteria No. 2: Previous Problems During Recovery

Despite participating in a past addiction recovery, have you experienced such severe pain or problems that you became fearful you might:

1. Start using alcohol or other drugs to medicate the pain and manage the problems?
2. Actually start using alcohol and/or other drugs?
3. Decide to stop your relapse and get back into recovery?
4. **Hidden Relapse Warning Signs:** In reviewing the above information did you notice anything that has or may have contributed to a relapse? ❑ Yes ❑ No

   Please list the three most important things you noticed that may have contributed to your relapse.

   A. The first thing I noticed that may have contributed to relapse is...

   ____

   ____

   B. The second thing I noticed that may have contributed to relapse is...

   ____

   ____

   C. The third thing I noticed that may have contributed to relapse is...

   ____

   ____

Criteria No. 3: Currently Abstinent and Stable

1. Are you currently abstinent from alcohol and other drugs? When did you last use?

   ____

2. Are you able to *think* clearly enough to benefit from education in relapse prevention therapy?

   ❑ I am sure. ❑ I think so, but not completely sure. ❑ I don't think I can.
   Please explain:

   ____

   ____

3. Can you discuss difficult or painful issues without losing control of your emotions and shutting down or overreacting?

   ❑ I am sure. ❑ I think so, but not completely sure. ❑ I don't think I can.
   Please explain:

   ____

   ____

4. Are you willing to commit to completing the relapse prevention therapy (RPT) process, which involves attending classes, doing homework between classes, and having individual sessions with your counselor as needed?

   ❑ Yes ❑ No ❑ Please explain:

   ____

   ____

5. **Hidden Relapse Warning Signs:** In reviewing the above information did you notice anything that has or may contribute to a relapse? ❑ Yes ❑ No

   Please list the three most important things you noticed that may have contributed to your relapse.

   A. The first thing I noticed that may have contributed to relapse was…

   ____

   ____

   B. The second thing I noticed that may have contributed to relapse was…

   ____

   ____

   C. The third thing I noticed that may have contributed to relapse was…

   ____

   ____

Exercise 2—Part B: Introducing the Relapse Warning Sign Card Process

For the remainder of this book you will need the *Warning Sign Identification Cards* in the Appendix of this workbook. Please take time now to remove them from the book so you have the stack readily accessible.

In this exercise we will show you how to start developing your first stack of warning sign cards. At this point we will be working only with *Titles* and *Descriptions* from side one of the cards. See a sample of side one of a *Warning Sign Identification Card* below. It is crucial that you do NOT work ahead and try to complete the other sections of the cards at this time. Please trust the process!

Warning Sign Identification Card (Side 1)

Title:____

Description: I know I am in trouble with my recovery when I…

____

Thought: When I experience this warning sign I tend to think…

____

Feeling: When I experience this warning sign I tend to feel…

____

Urge: When I experience this warning sign I have an urge to…

____

Action: When I experience this warning sign what I actually do is…

____

Reaction: I tend to invite others to become part of my problem by…

____

Exercise 2—Part C: Developing Your First Stack of Warning Sign Cards

Step 1: Review *Exercise 2: Learning from Past Efforts at Recovery*, and please fill out a separate card (using the directions below) for each of your three (3) answers in the **Hidden Relapse Warning Signs** sections for each of the three criteria. You should have nine (9) warning cards ready before you go to the next step.

Step 2: As you notice any automatic thoughts (hot responses) that may come while reviewing this information from the nine **Hidden Relapse Warning Signs** you will need to add a new warning sign card.

Step 3: Take your deck of Relapse Warning Sign Cards. On side one of the card is a place for the **Title** and the **Description** of the warning sign. We will work only with those two parts at this time.

Step 4: Take the initial list of nine (9) *Hidden Warning Sign Cards,* and any additional warning signs you added in step two. Read each one aloud. Ask yourself if you think each one is a warning sign that could set you up to become miserable in recovery or to experience a craving to use alcohol or other drugs. If you say yes, go to the next step.

Step 5: Prepare **A Personal Title** for each warning sign and put it in the **Title** space on side one of a card. A personal warning sign title is between one and five words and captures the nature of the warning sign. It acts as a title that easily will remind you of the warning sign when you think about it.

Step 6: Prepare **A Personal Description** for the warning sign.
A Personal Description is a sentence that:

A. Starts with the words, "I know I'm in trouble with my recovery when..."

B. Is a complete sentence.

C. Makes you the actor or subject of the sentence; i.e., "I know I am in trouble with my recovery when **I**..."

D. Describes a specific behavior or way of believing or thinking that creates a risk of relapse; i.e., "I know I'm in trouble with my recovery when I get angry and defensive when my spouse wants to know about my day."

Step 7: Read the title and description aloud three times, taking a breath between each repetition to observe any feelings you are having or images that come to mind when you say them. The goal is for the title and description to be in your own words so that they feel right to you when you read them aloud.

Step 8: Put the card in the stack and proceed to the next warning sign on your list. Repeat the process until you have reviewed all warning signs.

Exercise 2—Part D: Jill and Phil's Initial Nine Warning Sign Cards

Jill's Warning Sign Cards	Phil's Warning Sign Cards
1. Title: AA Sucks Description: "I know I'm in trouble with my recovery when I tell myself I don't need to go to my meetings."	1. Title: No! Not Me! Description: "I know I'm in trouble with my recovery when I start looking for all the *good* reasons why I'm not really addicted."

2. Title: Doomed Description: "I know I'm in trouble with my recovery when I tell myself nobody can help me. It's hopeless, so why try?"	2. Title: Here We Go Again Description: "I know I'm in trouble with my recovery when I start telling myself 'What's the use?' I've tried this so many times and always fail."
3. Title: Roller Coaster Ride Description: "I know I'm in trouble with my recovery when I can't turn off my feelings and take things out on others."	3. Title: Under the Radar Description: "I know I'm in trouble with my recovery when I start saying what others want to hear so I can do what I want and be comfortable."
4. Title: Fatal Attraction Description: "I know I'm in trouble with my recovery when I start focusing on all the good things drinking does for me and how much I miss it."	4. Title: Kicking and Screaming Description: "I know I'm in trouble with my recovery when I convince myself of all the good reasons why I should be allowed to drink and use the way I want, and nobody has a right to stop me."
5. Title: Going Crazy Description: "I know I'm in trouble with my recovery when my mind starts racing, and I can't shut it down."	5. Title: Just Until Description: "I know I'm in trouble with my recovery when I tell myself I'll stop for now, but as soon as I feel better and the pressure is off I can start again."
6. Title: Sneaking Drinking Description: "I know I'm in trouble with my recovery when I believe no one will know if I just have one glass of wine."	6. Title: The Blame Game Description: "I know I'm in trouble with my recovery when I tell myself that it's not my fault I relapsed this time."
7. Title: Hiding Out Description: "I know I'm in trouble with my recovery when I refuse to talk about my problems with anybody."	7. Title: Too Hot to Handle Description: "I know I'm in trouble with my recovery when I believe I need to escape from my painful feelings."
8. Title: Space Cadet Description: "I know I'm in trouble with my recovery when I can't focus on what I need to be doing, and my life continues to be out of control."	8. Title: Not Really Sure Description: "I know I'm in trouble with my recovery when I start listing all the great reasons I don't need treatment at this time; I can handle this on my own."
9. Title: If Only Description: "I know I'm in trouble with my recovery when I can't stop thinking how great life would be if I could keep drinking the way I want."	9. Title: Liar, Liar Pants on Fire Description: "I know I'm in trouble with my recovery when I start making up reasons why I don't need anybody's help because I know so much about recovery."

After completing these initial nine cards both Jill and Phil went on to develop several new hot response cards. Please take the time to review their initial nine titles and descriptions. Then make sure your first stack of cards is as complete as possible.

This exercise ends here.

Exercise No. 3: Life and Addiction History

Instructions:

1. Many people relapse because they have life problems they've never learned to understand or cope with.
2. Some of these problems come back, over and over in a seemingly endless cycle.
3. The purpose of completing the *Life and Addiction History* is to identify *the pattern of recurring life problems* that sets you up to relapse.
4. The following questions will help you think about your life and the recurring pattern of problems you have experienced. It also will help you to understand how you used alcohol or other drugs (AODs) to cope with these problems.
5. *Your goal is to identify recurring patterns of problems*. To accomplish this goal, you'll need to look at your life in a different way.
6. You'll need to see the big picture of your life, starting with your birth and moving through all the major changes and decisions you have made to create your current life circumstances.
7. In this exercise we will ask you to look at each stage of your life in a way that will help you identify the important patterns or cycles of events more clearly.

Exercise 3—Part A: Developing Your Life and Addiction History

Stages of Life	Alcohol and Other Drug Use
1. Childhood	**1. Childhood**
A. What was your *childhood* like? __________ __________ __________ B. My primary *strengths* during childhood: 1) __________ 2) __________ 3) __________ C. My primary *weaknesses* during childhood: 1) __________ 2) __________ 3) __________ D. The most important thing I *learned about myself* during childhood was: __________ __________ __________	A. Did you know of anyone who drank or used drugs when you were a child? [ ] Yes [ ] No Who? __________ B. What benefits did you think they were getting from using AODs? __________ __________ C. What disadvantages did you think they were getting from using AODs? __________ __________ D. What is the most important thing you *learned about AODs* during your childhood? __________ __________ __________ __________
2. Grammar School	**2. Grammar School**
A. What was *grammar school* like? __________ __________ __________ B. My primary *strengths* were: 1) __________ 2) __________ 3) __________ C. My primary *weaknesses* were: 1) __________ 2) __________ 3) __________	A. What did you want alcohol or other drugs to do for you during this period? __________ B. Did you get what you wanted? Please explain. __________ C. What were the benefits of using alcohol and drugs during this period? __________ D. What were the disadvantages of using alcohol and drugs during this period? __________

D. The most important thing I *learned about myself* in grammar school was: __________ __________ __________	E. What is the most important thing you *learned about alcohol and drugs* during this period? __________ __________ __________ __________ __________
3. High School	**3. High School**
A. What was *high school* like? __________ __________ __________ B. My primary *strengths* were: 1) __________ 2) __________ 3) __________ C. My primary *weaknesses* were: 1) __________ 2) __________ 3) __________ D The most important thing I *learned about myself* during high school was? __________ __________ __________	A. What did you want alcohol or other drugs to do for you during this period? __________ B. Did you get what you wanted? Please explain: __________ C. What were the benefits of using alcohol and drugs during this period? __________ D. What were the disadvantages of using alcohol and drugs during this period? __________ E. What is the most important thing you *learned about alcohol and drugs* during this period? __________ __________ __________ __________ __________
4. College	**4. College**
A. What was *college* like? __________ __________ __________ B. My primary *strengths* were: 1) __________	

2) ______

3) ______

C. My primary *weaknesses* were:

1) ______

2) ______

3) ______

D. The most important thing I *learned about myself* in college was?

______

______

______

A. What did you want alcohol or other drugs to do for you during this period?

______

B. Did you get what you wanted? Please explain:

______

C. What were the benefits of using alcohol and drugs during this period?

______

D. What were the disadvantages of using alcohol and drugs during this period?

______

E. What is the most important thing you *learned about yourself* during this period?

______

F. What is the most important thing you *learned about alcohol and drugs* during this period?

______

5. Military *(If you served)*

A. What was the *military* like?

______

______

______

B. My primary *strengths* were:

1) ______

2) ______

3) ______

C. My primary *weaknesses* were:

1) ______

2) ______

3) ______

D. The most important thing I *learned about myself* in the military was?

______

______

______

5. Military *(If you served)*

A. What did you want alcohol or other drugs to do for you during this period?

______

B. Did you get what you wanted? Please explain:

______

C. What were the benefits of using alcohol and drugs during this period?

______

D. What were the disadvantages of using alcohol and drugs during this period?

______

E. What is the most important thing you *learned about yourself* during this period?

______

F. What is the most important thing you *learned about alcohol and drugs* during this period?

______

______

6. Adult Work History

A. Describe your *adult work history*.

____

____

____

B. My primary *strengths* were:

1) ______________________________

2) ______________________________

3) ______________________________

C. My primary *weaknesses* were:

1) ______________________________

2) ______________________________

3) ______________________________

D. The most important thing I *learned about myself* as a result of working was:

____

____

____

6. Adult Work History

A. What did you want alcohol or other drugs to do for you during this period?

____

B. Did you get what you wanted? Please explain:

____

C. What were the benefits of using alcohol and drugs during this period?

____

D. What were the disadvantages of using alcohol and drugs during this period?

____

E. What is the most important thing you *learned about yourself* during this period?

____

F. What is the most important thing you *learned about alcohol and drugs* during this period?

____

7. Adult Relationship History

A. Briefly describe what your *adult relationships* are like.

1) ______________________________

2) ______________________________

3) ______________________________

B. My primary *strengths* are:

1) ______________________________

2) ______________________________

3) ______________________________

C. My primary *weaknesses* are:

1) ______________________________

2) ______________________________

3) ______________________________

7. Adult Relationship History

A. What did you want alcohol or other drugs to do for you during this period?

____

B. Did you get what you wanted? Please explain:

____

C. What were the benefits of using alcohol and drugs during this period?

____

D. What were the disadvantages of using alcohol and drugs during this period?

____

E. What is the most important thing you *learned about yourself* during this period?

____

D. The most important thing I *learned about myself* in adult relationships was: ____________________ ____________________ ____________________	F. What is the most important thing you *learned about alcohol and drugs* during this period? ____________________ ____________________ ____________________
8. Adult Family History	**8. Adult Family History**
A. Briefly describe your *family history*. 1) ____________________ 2) ____________________ 3) ____________________ B. My primary *strengths* are: 1) ____________________ 2) ____________________ 3) ____________________ C. My primary *weaknesses* are: 1) ____________________ 2) ____________________ 3) ____________________ D. The most important thing I *learned about myself* in family relationships was: ____________________ ____________________ ____________________	A. What did you want alcohol or other drugs to do for you during this period? ____________________ B. Did you get what you wanted? Please explain: ____________________ C. What were the benefits of using alcohol and drugs during this period? ____________________ D. What were the disadvantages of using alcohol and drugs during this period? ____________________ E. What is the most important thing you *learned about yourself* during this period? ____________________ F. What is the most important thing you *learned about alcohol and drugs* during this period? ____________________ ____________________
9. History of Adult Friendships	**8. History of Adult Friendships**
A. Briefly describe your *adult friendships*. 1) ____________________ 2) ____________________ 3) ____________________ B. My primary *strengths* are: 1) ____________________ 2) ____________________ 3) ____________________	A. What did you want alcohol or other drugs to do for you during this period? ____________________ B. Did you get what you wanted? [ ] Yes [ ] No ____________________ C. What were the benefits of using alcohol and drugs during this period? ____________________

C. My primary *weaknesses* are: 1) ____ 2) ____ 3) ____ D. The most important thing I *learned about myself* in adult relationships was: ____ ____ ____	D. What were the disadvantages of using alcohol and drugs during this period? ____ E. What is the most important thing you *learned about yourself* during this period? ____ F. What is the most important thing you *learned about alcohol and drugs* during this period? ____ ____
10. Overall Life History	**10. Overall Life History**
A. Write *three words* that describe what your life has been like. 1) ____ 2) ____ 3) ____ B. My primary *strengths* during this period of life were: 1) ____ 2) ____ 3) ____ C. My primary *weaknesses* during this period were: 1) ____ 2) ____ 3) ____	A. What did you want alcohol or other drugs to do for you in your life? ____ B. Did you get what you wanted? [ ] Yes [ ] No ____ C. What benefits did you get from using alcohol and drugs? ____ D. What disadvantages did you get from using alcohol and drugs? ____ E. What is the most important thing you *learned about yourself* during this period? ____ F. What is the most important thing you *learned about alcohol and drugs* during this period? ____ ____

Exercise 3—Part B: Summary of Your Life and Addiction History

Instructions: In this exercise you'll look for patterns in your life and addiction history of ongoing lifestyle problems that cause so much pain in recovery that you may start thinking about using alcohol or other drugs to handle the pain. Review your Life and Addiction History and answer the following questions:

1. What problems from your *childhood* followed you in recovery and set you up to relapse?

   ____

   ____

   ____

2. What problems from *grammar school* followed you into recovery and set you up to relapse?

   ____

   ____

   ____

3. What problems from *high school* followed you into recovery and set you up to relapse?

   ____

   ____

   ____

4. What problems from *college* followed you into recovery and set you up to relapse?

   ____

   ____

   ____

5. What problems from *military service* followed you into recovery and set you up to relapse?

   ____

   ____

   ____

6. What problems did you have as an *adult at work* that followed you into recovery and set you up to relapse?

   ____

   ____

   ____

7. What problems did you have in *adult intimate relationships* that followed you into recovery and set you up to relapse?

8. What problems did you have with *adult friendships* that followed you into recovery and set you up to relapse?

9. What problems did you have with your *family* that followed you into recovery and set you up to relapse?

10. What were the major things you wanted *relapse* to do for you that you couldn't do for yourself in recovery?

11. In the course of your life, what were the major things you wanted *alcohol and other drug use* to do for you that you couldn't do for yourself when sober?

12. What are the *most important things* you learned by completing this exercise?

Exercise 3—Part C: Preparing Your Second Stack of Cards

Step 1: Review the Life and Addiction History Summary. Focus on looking for any *Life and Addiction History—Hidden Relapse Warning Signs.*

Step 2: As you notice automatic thoughts (hot responses) that may come as you review this information, add them to your list of warning signs.

Step 3: Take your deck of Relapse Warning Sign cards. On side one of the card is a place for the **Title** and the **Description** of the warning sign. We will continue to work only with those two parts of the card at this time.

Step 4: Review your *List of Hidden Relapse Warning Signs* from the Life and Addiction History Summary and read each one aloud. Ask yourself if you think this might be a warning sign that could set you up to become miserable in recovery or to experience a craving to use alcohol or other drugs. If you say *yes*, go to the next step.

Step 5: Prepare **A Personal Title** for the warning sign and put it in the **Title** space on side one of the card. A personal warning sign is between one and five words and captures the nature of the warning sign. It acts as a title that will easily remind you of the warning sign when you think about it.

Step 6: Prepare **A Personal Description** for the warning sign.

A Personal Description is a sentence that:

A. Starts with the words, "I know I'm in trouble with my recovery when…"

B. Is a complete sentence.

C. Makes you the actor or subject of the sentence; i.e., "I know I am in trouble with my recovery when **I**…"

D. Describes a specific behavior or way of believing or thinking that creates a risk of relapse; i.e., "I know that I'm in trouble with my recovery when I get angry and defensive when my spouse wants to know about my day."

Step 7: Read the title and description aloud three times, taking a breath between each repetition. Observe any feelings you are having or images that come to mind when you say them. The goal is for the title and description to be in your own words so that they feel right to you when you read them aloud.

Step 8: Put the card in the stack and proceed to your next hidden warning sign. Repeat the process until you have reviewed all of the hidden warning signs from your Life and Addiction Summary.

Exercise 3—Part D: Ten of Jill and Phil's Warning Sign Cards

Jill's Warning Sign Cards	Phil's Warning Sign Cards
1. Title: Daddy Dearest Description: "I know I'm in trouble with my recovery when I start making up reasons to go visit my dad so I can check out his medicine cabinet."	1. Title: Bad Seed Description: "I know I'm in trouble with my recovery when I start convincing myself I don't deserve to be happy because I'm so screwed up."
2. Title: Needy Little Girl Description: "I know I'm in trouble with my recovery when I believe I need a man—any man—to be happy."	2. Title: Booze Happens Description: "I know I'm in trouble with my recovery when I start forgetting how I'm the one responsible for my own drinking problems."
3. Title: Doormat Description: "I know I'm in trouble with my recovery when I let others push me around and make excuses for them."	3. Title: Spider Web Description: "I know I'm in trouble with my recovery when I start telling lies to make myself look better, but it always catches up with me."
4. Title: Faking Bad Description: "I know I'm in trouble with my recovery when I start exaggerating my problems to get others to feel sorry for me and give me attention."	4. Title: Pushy Bitches Description: "I know I'm in trouble with my recovery when I start blaming the women in my life for all my problems and for nagging me."
5. Title: Beyond Help Description: "I know I'm in trouble with my recovery when I convince myself it's useless to keep trying because I'll never be happy."	5. Title: Stop the Music Description: "I know I'm in trouble with my recovery when I can't get all the voices from my past out of my head and just want to scream."
6. Title: Exhausted Description: "I know I'm in trouble with my recovery when I push myself so hard to help everyone else that I don't take care of myself and collapse."	6. Title: Sleepy Sleep Time Description: "I know I'm in trouble with my recovery when I want to crawl into bed and just stay there because when I'm asleep I don't hurt."
7. Title: Asleep at the Switch Description: "I know I'm in trouble with my recovery when I stop paying attention to what I really need to be doing."	7. Title: Gimme, Gimme, Gimme Description: "I know I'm in trouble with my recovery when I believe I deserve to have anything I want any time I want."
8. Title: Spinning out of Control Description: "I know I'm in trouble with my recovery when my brain is racing, and I can't turn off all my negative thoughts."	8. Title: Zero to Sixty Description: "I know I'm in trouble with my recovery when I'm always in a hurry and don't think things through the way I really should."

9. Title: My Little Runaway Description: "I know I'm in trouble with my recovery when all I can think about is escaping from everyone and everything that reminds me of my problems."	9. Title: It's not my Fault Description: "I know I'm in trouble with my recovery when I start blaming everyone for all of my problems so I don't have to change."
10. Title: Stand by Your Man Description: "I know I'm in trouble with my recovery when I find myself making excuses for why my husband is being mean to me."	10. Title: Scared Straight Description: "I know I'm in trouble with my recovery when I believe fear will keep me sober this time, but then I get really anxious, always living in fear."

After completing these 10 warning sign cards Jill and Phil followed the directions above and completed their second stack of cards. Please review their examples and go over your life and addiction-history summary again. Make sure you have a good second stack of cards ready to move forward. Remember, we are doing just titles and descriptions at this point.

Jill and Phil were concerned that some of their cards seemed very similar. They were told not to worry because we deal with duplications in a later exercise. The important thing for now is to get as many titles and description cards written as possible.

This exercise ends here.

Exercise No. 4: The Recovery and Relapse Calendar

Exercise 4—Part A: Completing Your Personalized Relapse Calendar

Instructions: Many relapse-prone people minimize or *awfulize* their memories of relapse. Those who minimize say to themselves, "I don't relapse very often, and when I do, it isn't very bad at all." Those who *awfulize* say to themselves, "I've relapsed so many times I couldn't even count them, and when I do relapse, I always lose everything."

The Relapse Calendar will help you remember how many relapse episodes you've had, what started them, and how long they lasted. A relapse episode is a period when you used alcohol or drugs that was followed by at least 10 days of abstinence.

Here's how you complete the calendar:

1. Enter the date of your first serious attempt at abstinence in the space indicated on the first line.
2. The first column gives you a place to enter the year. Starting with the year of your first serious attempt at abstinence, enter all the following years down to the present.
3. Following each year is a timeline with the months printed across the top. Locate the date of your first serious attempt at abstinence on the timeline and mark it with a hash mark (|).
4. Identify the point on the timeline when you returned to addictive use. Place another hash mark (|) at that point on the timeline. Connect the two hash marks with a solid horizontal line (————————) to represent this first period of abstinence.
5. Identify the next point on the timeline when you became abstinent, and mark it with a hash mark. Connect that with the previous hash mark using a jagged line (/\/\/\) to indicate this period of addictive use.
6. Mark all periods of abstinence with solid lines and all periods of addictive use with jagged lines. Be sure to include all periods of abstinence and all relapse episodes.
7. At the start of each period of abstinence, write a title for that abstinence period above the line.
8. At the start of each period of addictive use, write a title above the start of the jagged line.

First Serious Attempt at Abstinence: ______________________________

Year	Jan.	Feb.	March	April	May	June	July	Aug.	Sept.	Oct.	Nov.	Dec.

Year	Jan.	Feb.	March	April	May	June	July	Aug.	Sept.	Oct.	Nov.	Dec.

Exercise 4—Part B: Your Relapse Episode List

Instructions: This exercise will help you notice what happened when you tried not to use alcohol and drugs in the past. By understanding what happened during these times, you can see what to change. Refer to your completed relapse calendar while you do this exercise.

On the relapse calendar, find your three most recent relapse episodes and the periods of recovery before those episodes. When you're looking at a relapse episode it's important also to look at the period of recovery right before it. The period of recovery contains clues that help you understand why you relapsed. Just as we "hit a bottom" in addiction that leads into recovery, we also can "hit a bottom" in recovery if we don't have the right kind of support and skill training.

In this exercise each relapse episode and the period of recovery before it is called an "Attempt at Recovery/Relapse Episode." If you've had only two relapses, start with Section 2. If you've had only one relapse, start with Section 3.

Third-Most-Recent Recovery/Relapse Episode

1. Look at your relapse calendar. When did the period of recovery before your third-most-recent relapse begin? ____________________ (month and year)

2. Remember what you were thinking and feeling right before you decided to stop using alcohol and other drugs. What made you decide to stop using?

   ____

   ____

   ____

   A. What did you want sobriety to do for you that you couldn't do for yourself while you were actively using?

      ____

      ____

   B. What did you want to escape from or cope with by getting sober that you couldn't handle while you were actively using?

      ____

      ____

3. What did you do to stop using alcohol and other drugs and get into recovery?

   ____

   ____

   ____

4. What did you do on an ongoing basis to help yourself stay sober?

   ____

   ____

   ____

5. Remember what you were thinking and feeling right before you decided to start using alcohol and other drugs (your third-most-recent relapse). What made you decide to start using again?

____

____

   A. What did you want alcohol and other drugs to do for you that you couldn't do for yourself while you were sober?

   ____

   ____

   B. What did you want to escape from or cope with by using alcohol or drugs that you couldn't handle while you were sober?

   ____

   ____

6. When did you relapse? ____________ (month and year)

7. What was the main thing you wanted alcohol and drug use to help you do?

____

____

____

____

8. Did you get what you wanted by using alcohol and other drugs?

❑ Yes ❑ No ❑ Unsure

____

____

____

Second-Most-Recent Recovery/Relapse Episode

1. Look at your relapse calendar. When did the period of recovery before your most-recent relapse begin? ____________ (month and year)

2. Remember what you were thinking and feeling right before you decided to stop drinking and drugging. What made you decide to stop?

____

____

____

A. What did you want sobriety to do for you that you couldn't do for yourself while you were using alcohol and other drugs?

____

____

B. What did you want to escape from or cope with in sobriety that you couldn't while you were using alcohol and other drugs?

____

____

3. What did you do to stop alcohol and other drug use and get sober?

____

____

____

4. What did you do on an ongoing basis to help yourself stay sober?

____

____

____

5. Remember what you were thinking and feeling right before you decided to start using alcohol and other drugs (your most-recent relapse). What made you decide to start using?

____

____

A. What did you want alcohol and other drugs to do for you that you couldn't do for yourself while you were sober?

____

____

B. What did you want to escape from or cope with by using alcohol or drugs that you couldn't handle while you were sober?

____

____

6. When did you relapse? ____________________ (month and year)

7. What was the main thing you wanted the alcohol and other drugs to help you do?

____

____

____

8. What happened to you after you started using alcohol and other drugs?

____

____

____

9. Remember what you were thinking and feeling right before you decided to stop using alcohol or other drugs and get sober. What made you decide to get sober?

____

____

A. What did you want sobriety to do for you that you couldn't do for yourself while you were using alcohol and other drugs?

____

____

B. What did you want to escape from or cope with in sobriety that you couldn't handle while you were using alcohol or other drugs?

____

____

10. What did you do to stop using alcohol and other drugs and start getting sober?

____

____

____

Most-Recent Recovery/Relapse Episode

1. Look at your relapse calendar. When did the period of recovery before your most recent relapse begin? ____________________ (month and year)

2. Remember what you were thinking and feeling right before you decided to stop drinking and drugging. What made you decide to stop?

____

____

____

A. What did you want sobriety to do for you that you couldn't do for yourself while you were using alcohol and other drugs?

____

____

B. What did you want to escape from or cope with in sobriety that you couldn't while you were using alcohol and other drugs?

____

____

3. What did you do to stop alcohol and other drug use and get sober?

____

____

____

4. What did you do on an ongoing basis to help yourself stay sober?

____

____

____

5. Remember what you were thinking and feeling right before you decided to start using alcohol and other drugs (your most-recent relapse). What made you decide to start using?

____

____

A. What did you want alcohol and other drugs to do for you that you couldn't do for yourself while you were sober?

____

____

B. What did you want to escape from or cope with by using alcohol or drugs that you couldn't handle while you were sober?

____

____

6. When did you relapse? ____________________ (month and year)

7. What was the main thing you wanted the alcohol and other drugs to help you do?

____

____

____

8. What happened to you after you started using alcohol and other drugs?

____

____

____

9. Remember what you were thinking and feeling right before you decided to stop using alcohol or other drugs and get sober. What made you decide to get sober?

____

____

A. What did you want sobriety to do for you that you couldn't do for yourself while you were using alcohol and other drugs?

____

____

B. What did you want to escape from or cope with in sobriety that you couldn't handle while you were using alcohol or other drugs?

____

____

10. What did you do to stop using alcohol and other drugs and start getting sober?

____

____

Exercise 4—Part C: Summary of Your Relapse History

Instructions: In this exercise you'll look for any patterns in your reasons for returning to alcohol or drug use in the past. Review your Relapse Calendar and Relapse Episode List and answer the following questions.

1. When was your first attempt at recovery? ______________ (month and year)
2. Since that time, how many times have you tried to recover and relapsed? _____
3. What's the longest period you've stayed in recovery? ______________
4. What were your reasons for stopping the relapses and getting back in recovery?

____

____

____

5. What were the major things you wanted recovery to do for you that you couldn't do for yourself in relapse?

____

____

____

6. What were the major things you wanted to escape from or cope with in recovery that you couldn't escape from or cope with in relapse?

____

____

____

7. What were the major things you wanted relapse to do for you that you couldn't do for yourself in recovery?

____

____

____

8. What were the major things you wanted to escape from or cope with by relapsing that you couldn't escape from or cope with in recovery?

9. Look at the summary section of your Life and Addiction History (page 31). List the positive things you believed that addictive use could do for you.

10. How do those things compare with what you wanted relapse to do for you? (Question 7 above)

11. Look again at the summary section of your Life and Addiction History. List the negative or painful things you believed that addictive use could help you stop doing, escape from, or cope with.

12. How do those things compare with the negative or painful things you wanted to escape from or cope with by relapsing? (Question 8 above)

13. What are the most important things you learned by completing this exercise?

14. What things have you identified in this exercise that increase your risk of relapsing while you're in recovery?

Exercise 4—Part D: Preparing Your Third Stack of Cards

Step 1: Review the summary of the Recovery and Relapse History while looking at *The Recovery & Relapse History—Hidden Warning Signs.*

Step 2: As you notice automatic thoughts (hot responses) that may come in reviewing this information, add them to the list of *Hidden Relapse Warning Signs*.

Step 3: Take your deck of Relapse Warning Sign cards. On side one of the card is a place for the **Title** and the **Description** of the warning sign. You will work only with those two parts at this time.

Step 4: Review your *List of Hidden Relapse Warning Signs* and read each one aloud. Ask yourself if you think this might be a warning sign that could set you up to become miserable in recovery or to experience a craving to use alcohol or other drugs. If the answer is *yes* go to the next step.

Step 5: Prepare **A Personal Title** for the warning sign and put in the **Title** space on side one of the card. A personal warning sign is between one and five words and captures the nature of the warning sign. It acts as a title that will easily remind you of the warning sign when you think about it.

Step 6: Prepare **A Personal Description** for the warning sign. A Personal Description is a sentence that:

A. Starts with the words, "I know I'm in trouble with my recovery when..."

B. Is a complete sentence.

C. Makes you the actor or subject of the sentence; i.e., "I know I am in trouble with my recovery when **I**..."

D. Describes a specific behavior or way of believing or thinking that creates a risk of relapse; i.e., "I know I'm in trouble with my recovery when I get angry and defensive when my spouse wants to know about my day."

Step 7: Read the title and description aloud three times, taking a breath between each repetition to note any feelings you are having or images that come to mind when you say them. The goal is for the title and description to be in your own words so they feel right to you when you read them aloud.

Step 8: Put the card in the stack and proceed to the next *Hidden Relapse Warning Sign.* Repeat the process until you have reviewed all hidden warning signs.

Exercise 4—Part E: Ten of Jill and Phil's Recovery/Relapse Warning Sign Cards

Jill's Warning Sign Cards	Phil's Warning Sign Cards
1. Title: Turn out the Lights, Party's Over Description: "I know I'm in trouble with my recovery when I realize the game's over and I really can't drink or use anymore, and then I get very afraid."	1. Title: What Now? Description: "I know I'm in trouble with my recovery when I think everyone is out to get me, and anything that can go wrong does, and I get really mad."
2. Title: Woe Is Me Description: "I know I'm in trouble with my recovery when I keep putting myself in the victim role and try to convince others how bad my life is."	2. Title: Damn Them to Hell Description: "I know I'm in trouble with my recovery when I start blaming others for all of my problems and want to punish them."
3. Title: What's in It for Me Description: "I know I'm in trouble with my recovery when I disregard the needs of my kids because I just want to escape."	3. Title: Desperation Fascination Description: "I know I'm in trouble with my recovery when I convince myself I really need to hang out with my exciting old drinking and using buddies."
4. Title: Checking Out Description: "I know I'm in trouble with my recovery when I can't stay focused on what I need to do to take care of myself and end up desperate."	4. Title: The Solution Description: "I know I'm in trouble with my recovery when I see alcohol and drug use as the best way to cope with my pain and suffering."
5. Title: Safe Haven, My Ass Description: "I know I'm in trouble with my recovery when I start thinking that going to visit my dad is a good idea."	5. Title: Little Tin God Description: "I know I'm in trouble with my recovery when I believe I'm the only one who really knows what's best for me."
6. Title: Alone Again—Naturally Description: "I know I'm in trouble with my recovery when I isolate from anyone who will tell me the truth that I really don't want to hear, and then I get resentful when they're not there for me."	6. Title: How Low Can I Go? Description: "I know I'm in trouble with my recovery when I can't see the problems I keep creating for myself, and I just keep spiraling down and down."
7. Title: Fallen Angel Description: "I know I'm in trouble with my recovery when I do self-destructive things and disappoint those who love me, and then I feel like a real loser."	7. Title: Trauma and Drama Description: "I know I'm in trouble with my recovery when I start creating bad problems so others won't look at what's really going on with me."

8. Title: Looking Good on the Outside Description: "I know I'm in trouble with my recovery when I start putting on a show to stop others from knowing me."	8. Title: Shame, Shame, Shame Description: "I know I'm in trouble with my recovery when I realize how bad I'm screwing up, and I want to run and hide."
9. Title: The Great Escape Description: "I know I'm in trouble with my recovery when I start looking for ways to not honor my recovery commitments and justify it to others."	9. Title: Bad to the Bone Description: "I know I'm in trouble with my recovery when I start hanging out with dangerous people and doing things that hurt those I love."
10. Title: Broken Dreams Description: "I know I'm in trouble with my recovery when I remember all of the ways I sabotaged myself and my family and start thinking, 'What's the use?'"	10. Title: Recovery Sucks Description: "I know I'm in trouble with my recovery when I can see only the down side of sobriety and start glamorizing my past."

After completing these 10 warning sign cards Jill and Phil followed the directions above and completed their third stack of cards. Please review their examples. Go over your recovery and relapse history summary again and make sure you have a good third stack of cards ready to move forward. Remember, we still are doing just titles and descriptions at this point.

This was a very eye-opening exercise for Jill and Phil. Phil started getting very depressed and upset with himself as he looked at all the times he went through a treatment program and then ignored what he learned shortly after completing the program. Jill at first became angry with herself and then hopeful when she started seeing many of the self-defeating patterns that followed her from childhood. Both Jill and Phil started seeing that alcohol and other drug use was but the tip of the iceberg for them.

Please start being aware of your self-defeating patterns. See how many you can identify that are similar, or even identical, to the ones you uncovered in your life and addiction history. Like Jill and Phil you may discover many of your self-defeating patterns have nothing to do with your alcohol or other drug use. But they do cause you unnecessary pain and problems, and you eventually will see alcohol or other drugs providing the solution.

This exercise ends here.

Exercise No. 5: Review of the Warning Sign List

Instructions: Read the following warning sign list aloud. It would be very helpful to do this with your therapist, coach, or appropriate significant other taking turns to read each one.

1. **Making Progress in Recovery:** At first I work my recovery program, and it helps me to stay sober and live a better life. My program helps me feel better. It allows me to handle problems I had trouble with before. I start getting better at dealing with people and situations in a sober, honest, responsible, and effective way.

2. **Hitting Stuck-Points in Recovery:** After awhile I get stuck in my recovery. I experience problems, and I can't motivate myself to do what I know I need to do to solve them in a sober and responsible way. I go through the motions of working my recovery problem when other people are around, but I privately start to believe that working my program isn't as important as it used to be. After awhile, I start using my old ways of thinking, managing feelings, and behaving that make me look good on the outside but leave me feeling bad on the inside. I keep my bad feelings a secret.

3. **High-Stress Reactions:** I start feeling more tense or more stressed than before, but I don't tell anyone. My stress levels start to get so high that I can't function normally. My moods swing from feeling on top of the world to feeling like nothing is working out. Deep inside I start to think something is wrong, and I should get some help. But I decide to ignore these thoughts, stuff my feelings, and hide what I'm experiencing from others.

4. **Return to Denial:** I stop doing the things that helped me get clean and sober—I stop growing. I start thinking I might be cured and don't have to keep doing all this recovery stuff. I stop paying attention to or honestly telling others what I'm thinking and feeling. I start worrying about the changes in my thinking, feelings, and behavior. I don't want to think about it or talk about it. I go into denial and try to convince myself that everything is OK, though I know it isn't. At times a debate goes on in my head between my sober self and my addictive self.

5. **Addictive Beliefs and Perceptions:** As my stress goes up, my old, self-defeating belief system comes to life. I start to believe I'm cured and I can use alcohol or other drugs safely in a controlled or moderate fashion. I start to believe that I don't need to work a recovery program and mistakenly believe nothing bad will happen if I experiment with social drinking or recreational drug use. My perceptions or insights about myself and recovery become distorted.

6. **Irrational and Self-Defeating Thinking:** These self-defeating beliefs begin showing in what I think and what I say to others. I use relapse justifications to convince myself that it is OK if I decide to use alcohol or other drugs, or that I have no choice but to start using self-defeating behaviors. I may start using my old, impulsive and compulsive behaviors. I cause myself so much unnecessary pain and create so many unnecessary problems that I start to think that staying in recovery isn't worth the effort.

7. **Urges to Use:** I start feeling *deprivation anxiety* (caused by the addictive belief that I never can have a good life when sober), *boredom with sobriety* (based on the addictive belief that nothing fun, meaningful, or exciting can happen without alcohol or other drugs), and *craving* (a strong desire to use caused by thinking about how good it used to be and imagining how good things would be in the future if I started using again).

8. **Social Isolation:** I start pushing away people who want to help me stay sober. I stop participating in activities that help me protect my sobriety. I stop attending recovery

support groups and stop professional counseling or therapy. I start attracting and feeling attracted to people, places, and things that support my addictive thinking and make it easy for me to get or use alcohol or other drugs.

9. **Inner Conflict:** I begin to feel an inner conflict between my *sober self* who knows something is going wrong and tells me to get help, and my *addictive self*, who tells me everything is fine, and I shouldn't worry. I start fantasizing that if things get bad enough I can use my drug of choice to feel better. But I quickly push these thoughts from my mind and tell myself I am cured or recovered from addiction and never would drink or use drugs again.

10. **Crisis Building and Irrational Behavior:** I start having problems that I don't understand. Though I want to solve these problems and I work hard at it, two new problems pop up to replace every problem I solve. I can't see the big picture, and I start doing things that won't help. I feel depressed and try to distract myself by getting busy with other things and not talking about the depression. I stop planning ahead. Things keep going wrong, and I feel like nothing is going my way. No matter how hard I try, nothing seems to work. I think that using alcohol and other drugs will make me feel better and solve my problems. I try to put these thoughts about relapse out of my mind, but sometimes they're so strong that I can't stop them. I start to believe that relapsing is the only way to keep myself from going crazy or killing myself. Relapsing actually looks like a sane and rational alternative.

11. **Immobilization:** I feel trapped in an endless stream of unmanageable problems. I get tired of putting time and energy into things that aren't working. I feel like giving up. I can't seem to get started or make myself do the things I know I need to do. I exaggerate small problems. I can't force myself to deal with the major things that could make a difference. I begin to feel like a failure who can't do anything right. I start wishing I could run away or that something magical would happen to rescue me from my problems.

12. **Experiencing Painful Problems:** I have trouble thinking clearly and solving usually simple problems. Sometimes my mind races, and I can't shut it off. Other times I go blank and can't concentrate on anything. I have trouble remembering things. I switch from overreacting to feeling emotionally numb. I start to think I might be going crazy. I stop trusting my feelings and try to ignore stuff, or forget about it. I start making bad decisions that I wouldn't have made if I were thinking clearly. I become easily angered and start to take it out on my friends and family. I get irritated with other people because they don't understand me and can't seem to help me. My problems only get worse.

13. **Return to Addictive Thinking:** I start doing things that violate my values, hurt me, and hurt those I love. As a result, I start losing respect for myself. I find excuses to miss therapy and self-help group meetings. I cut myself off from others by ignoring them, getting angry with them, or criticizing and putting them down. I get so isolated that it seems there's no one to turn to for help. I start to feel sorry for myself and use self-pity to get attention. I feel ashamed and guilty. I know I'm out of control, but I keep lying, using denial, and making excuses for my behavior. I feel trapped by the pain and start to believe that I'll never be able to manage my life. I see only three possible ways out—insanity, suicide, or relapse. I no longer believe anyone or anything else can help me. No matter how hard I try to regain control, I'm unable to do so.

14. **High-Risk Situations:** Things seem so bad that I begin to think I might as well relapse because things couldn't get worse. I start to think that using alcohol or other drugs will make me feel better and help me manage my pain and solve my problems. I try to con-

vince myself that I can use alcohol or other drugs without losing control or developing serious problems, though deep inside I know I can't. So I start putting myself into high-risk situations where I am surrounded by people who are using and encouraging me to use. I know it's only a matter of time before I give in and use because I have removed myself from all of my sobriety support systems.

15. **Relapse:** I try to solve my problems and feel better by using alcohol or other drugs. Although I rationalize my behavior, deep inside I know using alcohol or other drugs won't work and will hurt me in the long run. I start the relapse and try to control my behavior. I feel myself losing control and get disappointed because the relapse isn't doing for me what I thought it would. My relapse spirals out of control, creating severe problems with my life and health. The problems continue to get worse until I realize that I need help and decide to try recovery one more time.

Exercise 5—Part A: Developing Your Initial Warning Sign List

Instructions: Review the warning signs on the *Warning Sign List*. Select three warning signs you believe most apply to you and answer the following questions. Be prepared to present your answers to your therapist or relapse prevention coach.

First Warning Sign on the Initial Warning Sign List

1. What is the first warning sign you selected? Copy the title directly from the *Relapse Warning Sign List.*

   ____

2. Why did you select this warning sign?

   ____

   ____

3. Read the description of the warning sign again and underline what you consider the most-important word or phrase. What word or phrase did you underline?

   ____

4. What does this word or phrase mean to you?

   ____

   ____

5. Write a *personal title* for the warning sign that will be easy to remember. The title should be no longer than two or three words.

   ____

6. Write a *personal description* for the warning sign you selected. Make sure the description is a single sentence that begins with *I know I'm in trouble with my recovery when....* It's important not to use any words from the personal title in this description.

   ____

   ____

   ____

   ____

7. How do you change when you experience this warning sign?

____

____

8. What do you tend to think when you experience this warning sign?

____

____

9. What feelings do you usually have when you experience this warning sign?

____

____

❑	Strong	or	❑	Weak ______	❑	Fulfilled	or	❑	Frustrated ______
❑	Angry	or	❑	Caring ______	❑	Proud	or	❑	Ashamed ______
❑	Happy	or	❑	Sad ______	❑	Lonely	or	❑	Connected ______
❑	Safe	or	❑	Threatened ______	❑	Peaceful	or	❑	Agitated ______

10. What do you have an urge to do when you experience this warning sign?

____

____

11. What do you usually do when you experience this warning sign?

____

____

____

____

12. How do other people usually react to you when you experience this warning sign?

____

____

Second Warning Sign on the Initial Warning Sign List

1. What is the second warning sign you selected? Copy the title directly from the *Relapse Warning Sign List.*

____

2. Why did you select this warning sign?

____

____

3. Read the description of the warning sign again and underline what you consider the most important word or phrase. What word or phrase did you underline?

____

4. What does this word or phrase mean to you?

____

____

5. Write a *personal title* for the warning sign that will be easy to remember. The title should be no longer than two or three words.

____

6. Write a *personal description* for the warning sign you selected. Make sure the description is a single sentence that begins with the words, *I know I'm in trouble with my recovery when....* It's important not to use any words from the personal title in this description.

____

____

____

____

____

____

7. How do you change when you experience this warning sign?

____

____

8. What do you tend to think when you experience this warning sign?

____

____

9. What feelings do you usually have when you experience this warning sign?

____

____

❑ Strong	or	❑ Weak	______	❑ Fulfilled	or	❑ Frustrated	______
❑ Angry	or	❑ Caring	______	❑ Proud	or	❑ Ashamed	______
❑ Happy	or	❑ Sad	______	❑ Lonely	or	❑ Connected	______
❑ Safe	or	❑ Threatened	______	❑ Peaceful	or	❑ Agitated	______

10. What do you have an urge to do when you experience this warning sign?

____

____

11. What do you usually do when you experience this warning sign?

12. How do other people usually react to you when you experience this warning sign?

Third Warning Sign on the Initial Warning Sign List

1. What is the third warning sign you selected? Copy the title directly from the *Relapse Warning Sign List.*

2. Why did you select this warning sign?

3. Read the description of the warning sign again and underline what you consider the most important word or phrase. What word or phrase did you underline?

4. What does this word or phrase mean to you?

5. Write a *personal title* for the warning sign that will be easy to remember. The title should be no longer than two or three words.

6. Write a *personal description* for the warning sign you selected. Make sure the description is a single sentence that begins with the words *I know I'm in trouble with my recovery when....* It's important not to use any words from the personal title in this description.

7. How do you change when you experience this warning sign?

____

____

8. What do you tend to think when you experience this warning sign?

____

____

9. What feelings do you usually have when you experience this warning sign?

____

____

❑ Strong	or	❑ Weak ______	❑ Fulfilled	or	❑ Frustrated ______
❑ Angry	or	❑ Caring ______	❑ Proud	or	❑ Ashamed ______
❑ Happy	or	❑ Sad ______	❑ Lonely	or	❑ Connected ______
❑ Safe	or	❑ Threatened ______	❑ Peaceful	or	❑ Agitated ______

10. What do you have an urge to do when you experience this warning sign?

____

____

11. What do you usually do when you experience this warning sign?

____

____

____

____

12. How do other people usually react to you when you experience this warning sign?

____

____

Exercise 5—Part B: Jill and Phil's Initial Three Warning Sign Cards

Jill's Warning Sign Cards	Phil's Warning Sign Cards
1. **Return to Denial** Jill's Title: Honest Dishonesty Description: "I know I'm in trouble with my recovery when I *conveniently* forget what got me where I'm at in my recovery, and I stop working so hard."	1. **Hitting Stuck-Points In Recovery** Phil's Title: Resting on my Laurels Description: "I know I'm in trouble with my recovery when I run into a problem, don't want to work for a solution, and end up hurting myself and others."
2. **Inner Conflict** Jill's Title: Split Personality Description: "I know I'm in trouble with my recovery when I fight with myself in my head and don't really listen to my recovery voice."	2. **Relapse** Title: Magical Thinking Description: "I know I'm in trouble with my recovery when I convince myself that drinking and using is the best way to live my life and cope with my problems."
3. **Experiencing Painful Problems** Title: Bad Choices Description: "I know I'm in trouble with my recovery when I give in to my addict voice, start making bad decisions, and wonder why I'm in trouble again."	3. **Social Isolation** Title: Building a Wall Description: "I know I'm in trouble with my recovery when I start pulling away from my sponsor and other recovery friends and hide out all alone."

After completing these three warning sign cards Jill and Phil followed the directions above and moved to Part C to develop their fourth stack of cards. Jill and Phil were very surprised how much they identified to almost all 15 warning signs. The three they picked were the ones they saw that caused them the most trouble in the past and allowed them to relapse despite their desire to be in recovery.

Please review their examples and then go over the *Warning Sign List* again. Make sure you pick and personalize three warning signs that apply to you and identify all of the possible hidden warning signs.

After you answer all questions in the previous section you should have several new hidden warning signs. You can use them to build your fourth stack of cards, get ready to move forward, and develop your initial warning sign sequence. Remember, we still are doing just titles and descriptions.

Exercise 5—Part C: Preparing Your Fourth Stack of Cards

Instructions: Review the answers to each question answered for all three warning signs and ask yourself: "Are there any specific relapse warning signs hidden in this answer?" If the answer is *yes,* write a word, phrase, or sentence below that will help you remember the warning sign later.

Be sure to do this process with all twelve questions. Here is the process you will follow:

Step 1: Review the answer to the questions about each of the three warning signs while looking at *Warning Sign Analysis—Finding the Hidden Relapse Warning Signs.*

Step 2: As you notice automatic thoughts (hot responses) that may come while reviewing this information, add them to the list of hidden warning signs.

Step 3: Take your deck of *Relapse Warning Sign* cards. On Side 1 of the card is a place for the **Title** and the **Description** of the warning sign. You will work only with those two parts at this time.

Step 4: Take the *List of Hidden Relapse Warning Signs* and read each one aloud. Ask yourself if you think this might be a warning sign that could set you up to become miserable in recovery or to experience a craving to use alcohol or other drugs. If *yes* go to the next step.

Step 5: Prepare **A Personal Title** for the warning sign and put it in the **Title** space on side one of the card. A personal warning sign is one to five words and captures the nature of the warning sign. It acts as a title that easily will remind you of the warning sign when you think about it.

Step 6: Prepare **A Personal Description** for the warning sign. A Personal Description is a sentence that:

A. Starts with the words, "I know I'm in trouble with my recovery when…"

B. Is a complete sentence.

C. Makes you the actor or subject of the sentence; i.e., "I know I am in trouble with my recovery when I…"

D. Describes a specific behavior or way of believing or thinking that creates a risk of relapse; i.e., "I know I'm in trouble with my recovery when I get angry and defensive when my spouse wants to know about my day."

Step 7: Read the title and description aloud three times, taking a breath between each repetition to recognize any feelings you are having or images that come to mind when you say it. The goal is for the title and description to be in your own words so they feel right when you read them aloud.

Step 8: Put the card in the stack and proceed to the next hidden warning sign on the list. Repeat the process until you have reviewed all hidden warning signs.

Exercise 5—Part D: Developing Your Initial Warning Sign Card Sequence

Combining all the Stacks of Cards

1. Combining all of your Warning Sign Identification Cards.
   - A. Put all of your Warning Sign Identification cards in a pile next to you.
   - B. Notice that the front of each card has a place for a *title* (a word or short phrase that names the warning sign) and a *description* (a single sentence describing the warning sign that starts with the words *I know I'm in trouble with my recovery when...*)
   - C. In this exercise you will make sure you have a card with a title and a description for each hidden warning sign you found.
   - D. A *hidden warning sign* is something you do automatically without thinking about it or noticing it, and it increases your risk of relapse. For example, a hidden warning sign might be "I start working long hours" or "I start losing my temper a lot." Fill out a new card for any hidden warning signs you can see in your descriptions of this warning sign.
2. Review your stack of warning sign cards developed from:
   - A. The Warning Sign Cards
   - B. The Life and Addiction History
   - C. The Recovery and Relapse History
   - D. The Fifteen-Item Warning Sign List
3. Put the four stacks of cards together in one stack.
4. Each card contains part of a hidden warning sign. It may be a title or a description. It may be a thought, feeling, urge, or action statement related to another warning sign. As you place the cards in the order in which they typically occur you will notice how the cards relate to each other and begin creating a complete and coherent list.
   - A. Add the hidden warning sign cards that you identified and developed in question No. 1 above.
   - B. Make sure you have a personal title for each hidden warning sign on the card.
   - C. Make sure you have a personal description for each hidden warning sign on the line that starts with *I know I'm in trouble with my recovery when...*
   - D. Take a deep breath and read the title and description aloud several times. Make sure it feels right to you. If it doesn't feel right when you read it aloud, write it again on a new card, using different words that feel better to you or make more sense.
   - E. Keep starting new cards until you have sorted all prepared cards into chronological order (the sequence in which they tend to occur over time). If you're not sure about the order, take your best guess.
5. Arrange the cards in the order in which the warning signs generally happen. If two or more cards obviously describe the same warning sign, throw away all but one—or you can blend all of them into a new card.

6. Go through your cards one by one and read their titles and the descriptions.

   A. *Go visual!* Try to see yourself going through the sequence of activities the cards describe.

   B. Notice any *gaps in the action*. A gap is a skipped step in the action sequence. For example, there is a gap in the action between: "I start working long hours" and "I start losing my temper a lot."

   C. If you find gaps in the action, make new cards to fill them in. The gap described above might be filled with the warning signs "I start getting less and less sleep" and "I feel tired and irritable all of the time."

This exercise stops here.

Exercise No. 6: Developing Your Final Warning Sign Card Sequence

Important Note: For this exercise you need to use the *Warning Sign Identification Cards*. These cards are included in the index of this workbook. They also are available from Herald House/Independence Press in separate packets.

Exercise 6—Part A: Putting Together Your Final Warning Sign Card Sequence

The goal of this exercise is to help you develop a clear and concise warning sign card sequence of the situations, thoughts, feelings, and actions that lead you from stable recovery back to the use of alcohol and/or other drugs.

You develop the final warning sign card sequence by carefully reviewing the warning sign cards you have written up to this point. *The goal is to reduce the number of cards to between twelve and fifteen without leaving out any important things that lead you to relapse.*

The list is reduced by eliminating duplications and finding the warning sign cards that are actually thought, feeling, urge, action, or enabler statements related to other warning signs. Carefully write the final warning sign list by creating new and clearly written warning sign identification cards that will help you fill in anything missing in your first warning sign list.

To develop a clear and concise final warning sign card sequence, complete the following steps:

1. Check the Titles

Read your stack of *Warning Sign Identification Cards* and check to be sure that each card has a title. The title should be a word or a short phrase that's easy for you to remember and tells you exactly what the warning sign is all about. Good titles are short, clear, and easy to remember. Correct any titles that need it.

2. Check the Descriptions

Read the warning sign cards again. This time pay special attention to each description statement. Make sure the descriptions are clear by asking yourself the following questions about each card:

1. Is the description a complete sentence?
2. Does the sentence describe you doing something or wanting to do something, either by yourself or with (or to) someone or something else?
3. Are you the person who's doing the action in the warning sign? (What other people do or want to do are not warning signs for you. Your warning signs are *your* feelings and reactions to what they do.)
4. Did you use the same words in the title and the description? It is important to try to use different words in the title and the description. Rewrite the description if you need to.

3. Eliminate Duplications

You might end up like Jill and Phil and have several cards that are very similar. Read each warning sign card and notice if any other warning signs say about the same thing. Remember, *your goal is to end up with a final list of twelve to fifteen warning sign cards.* As you complete the following exercises, keep looking for warning signs that can be combined or eliminated.

4. Complete the Front of the Cards

On the front of each card, after the title and description, is a place for you to write a thought, feeling, urge, action, and enabling relationship (social reaction) statement. Starting with the first card, do the following:

1. **Thought Statement:** Read the title and the description and ask yourself what you're usually thinking when you experience that warning sign. Pick the most important thought and write it in the space next to the words, *"When I experience this warning sign I tend to think..."* Make sure the thought is written in a complete sentence. Now ask yourself these questions:

   A. Does the thought statement contain any *generalities*?

   B. Does the thought statement contain any *deletions*?

   C. Does the thought statement contain a *distorted metaphor (untrue story or tale)*?

   D. Is the thought statement really a feeling or emotion?

2. **Feeling Statement:** Read the title and description again and ask yourself what you usually feel when you experience this warning sign. Read your thought statement aloud several times and ask yourself, "What kinds of feelings will be caused by thinking this thought?" Write a feeling statement in the correct place that completes the statement, *"When I experience this warning sign I tend to feel..."* Use the feeling list to help you describe your feelings, and note how strongly you feel them on a scale of one to ten.

❑ Strong	or	❑ Weak ________		❑ Fulfilled	or	❑ Frustrated ______
❑ Angry	or	❑ Caring ________		❑ Proud	or	❑ Ashamed ______
❑ Happy	or	❑ Sad ________		❑ Lonely	or	❑ Connected ______
❑ Safe	or	❑ Threatened ______		❑ Peaceful	or	❑ Agitated ______

3. **Urge Statement:** Read the title and the description again and ask yourself, "What do I usually have an urge to do when I experience this warning sign?" Read the thought and feeling statement several times and ask yourself, "What are those thoughts and feelings likely to cause me to want to do about it?" Write the answer in the appropriate place. Write an urge statement in the correct place that completes the statement, *"When I experience this warning sign I have an urge to..."*

4. **Action Statement:** Read the title and the description again and ask yourself, "What do I actually do when I experience this warning sign?" Read the urge statement and ask

yourself, "Do I usually act out the urge or do I push the urge down and force myself to do something else?" Write an urge statement in the correct place that completes the statement, *"When I experience this warning sign what I actually do is..."*

5. **Reaction Statement:** Read the action statement again and ask yourself, "How are other people affected by what I do? How does my behavior invite other people to become part of my problem?" Write an enabling-relationship statement that completes the sentence, *"I tend to invite others to become part of my problem by..."*

5. Read the Next Warning Sign Card

The next warning sign card should describe an event that follows logically from the urge and action statements. The question you should ask yourself is, "How does what I do in response to the previous warning sign set me up to experience the next warning sign?"

6. Fill in Gaps in the Action

Slowly read the warning sign list again and see yourself moving through the sequence of events. Notice how you move from one warning sign to the next. Ask yourself, "Are there any gaps in the action? Do I skip a step anywhere in the process?" If you notice any gaps in the action, write new warning sign cards that will fill in those gaps. One way of filling in the gaps in action is to use the following method:

1. Identify the warning sign before and after the gap in the action.
2. Read the warning sign before the gap in the action and create a sentence stem that reads: *"One thing I do after (describe the action in the warning sign before the gap) is..."* This should bring to the surface the next step in the action sequence.
3. Read the warning sign after the gap in the action and create a sentence stem that reads: *"One thing that causes me to (describe the action in the warning sign after the gap) is..."* This should bring to the surface the previous step in the action sequence.
4. Review your answers to the sentence-completion exercise in steps 6-2 and 6-3 above and write one or more Warning Sign Cards that fill in the gap in the action.

7. Backtracking to Earlier Warning Signs

Look at the first warning sign card and ask yourself, "Is this really where it started? What happened that caused this first warning sign to happen?" If you can think of an earlier warning sign, write a new warning sign card that describes it. Read the sign you just wrote and ask, "What happened that caused this warning sign to happen?" If you can think of an earlier warning sign, write it below. Repeat this process until you can't think of any earlier warning signs.

8. Thinking about Relapse

Think about exactly how you talk yourself into relapse.

1. Number each card in the upper-right-hand corner so you easily can put them back in the order they're in, if you choose to.

2. Read each warning sign card again and ask yourself, "Do I start to think about relapsing when I experience this warning sign?" If the answer is yes, put the letter R (standing for relapse) at the top-right-hand corner of the card next to the number.

3. The warning signs that trigger an urge to relapse normally come near the end of the warning sign list. As an experiment, pull out each card that triggers an urge to relapse (those marked with an R). Put them at the end of the sequence, keeping them in the same order in relation to one another. In most cases this helps make the progression of warning sign cards clearer. If it doesn't work, put the cards back in the original order. If it does work, number the cards again in the upper-right-hand corner.

9. Reviewing Your Final Warning Sign Card Sequence

Read your warning sign cards one last time. You should clearly see that one warning sign causes the next one to occur. The first warning sign happens, and then we think self-defeating thoughts that cause us to have unmanageable feelings, which create the urge to act out the next warning sign.

10. Number Your Final Warning Sign Card Sequence

Using all of the previous information, sequence your warning sign cards in the order you believe they occur. Number them in pencil in the top-right-hand corner, starting with one. Please see how Jill and Phil completed their final warning sign card sequence on the following page.

Exercise 6—Part B: Jill and Phil's Final Warning Sign Card Sequence

Jill's Warning Sign Cards	Phil's Warning Sign Cards
1. Title: Standing Still in the Fast Lane Description: "I know I'm in trouble with my recovery when I convince myself I don't need to keep working so hard on my recovery and get complacent." T = "I'm fine." "I'm all better now." "I'm cured." "This sucks." F = Proud, excited, angry U = Slack off, procrastinate, hide out A = All of the above R = People get concerned, and I get angry at them but wonder if they're right.	**1. Title: Scared Straight** Description: "I know I'm in trouble with my recovery when I start believing fear will keep me sober this time, but then I get really anxious and live in fear." T = "I'll never drink/use again." "I know better now." "I only need to remember the last time." F = Hopeful, anxious, afraid U = Isolate, avoid meetings, stuff my feelings A = Hide out, lie to my recovery friends R = People try to help me, but I push them away.
2. Title: Split Personality Girl Description: "I know I'm in trouble with my recovery when I facilitate a debate in my head but don't listen to my recovery voice." T = "Recovery work sucks." "I don't need to work so hard." "Why bother?" F = Anger, fear, frustration U = Run away, stop sharing, look for people to side with me A = Stop going to meetings, stop talking to recovery support, obsessing on why AA sucks R = People try to share their concerns, but I don't listen or return their calls.	**2. Title: Under the Radar** Description: "I know I'm in trouble with my recovery when I tell others what I think they want to hear to keep them off my back." T = "It's none of their business." "I don't need them." "Leave me alone." F = Anger, frustration, anxiety, fear U = Run away, lash out, isolate A = Tell more lies, make excuses R = People start pulling away; I feel relieved at first and then start feeling guilty and afraid.

3. Title: Hiding Out Description: "I know I'm in trouble with my recovery when I refuse to talk about what's going on with me and start looking for enablers." T = "I don't need them." "AA sucks." "I need *real* friends." F = Anxious, afraid, frustrated, angry U = Stuff my feelings, hide out, look for enablers A = All of the above R = People are angry with me, but I don't care—I continue to seek enablers.	**3. Title: Building a Wall** Description: "I know I'm in trouble with my recovery when I keep pulling away from my sponsor and other recovery friends and hide out all alone." T = "I've got to get away." "I don't deserve help." "I need alone time." F = Anxious, afraid, ashamed, angry at myself U = Hide, stuff my feelings, run away A = Avoid my sponsor, beat myself up R = Everyone is concerned, but I won't believe them.
4. Title: Faking Bad Description: "I know I'm in trouble with my recovery when I start exaggerating my troubles to get others to feel sorry for me and give me attention." T = "I deserve help." "They don't care." "My life sucks." "I need to con them." F = Smug, anxious, excited, angry U = Lie and exaggerate, hide out, find distractions A = Start excessive shopping, isolate from support, lie to others, run away R = People start enabling me and feel sorry for me, but then I don't like it.	**4. Title: Bad Seed** Description: "I know I'm in trouble with my recovery when I tell myself I'm so screwed up that I don't deserve to be happy or have friends." T = "I'm screwed up." "I'm a loser." "Life sucks." "Nobody likes me." F = Anger, fear, guilt, shame U = Make excuses, lie, isolate, beat myself up A = Avoid others, beat myself up R = Others don't know what's going on with me, and I feel lonely and resentful.
5. Title: My Little Runaway Description: "I know I'm in trouble with my recovery when I start obsessing about escaping from everyone and everything." T = "I'm out of here." "I can't stand this." "They're all assholes." F = Afraid, angry, anxious, lonely U = Lash out, escape, hide, feel sorry for myself (have a pity party) A = Yell at others, have my pity party R = Others yell back and tell me how screwed up I am, and I believe them.	**5. Title: The Blame Game** Description: "I know I'm in trouble with my recovery when I get tired of feeling bad and convince myself that none of my problems are my fault; it's the women in my life." T = "It's not my fault." "Screw this." "If only they'd leave me alone." "Why are they doing this to me?" F = Anger, anxiety, fear, ashamed U = Lash out, find escapes, blame women A = Blame women, lie to myself R = Women try to rescue me, and I get angry.

6. Title: Woe Is Me Description: "I know I'm in trouble with my recovery when I mistakenly believe I'm worthless and let people victimize me." T = "I'm no good." "My life sucks." "I don't deserve to be happy." F = Sad, depressed, lonely, scared U = Look for diversions, shut down, isolate, cry A = Start obsessively looking for a man/diversion and hide out from recovery support people R = People get very concerned for me, men take advantage of me.	**6. Title: Pushy Bitches** Description: "I know I'm in trouble with my recovery when I keep blaming the women in my life for all my problems and especially for nagging me." T = "Screw them." "Why can't they leave me alone?" "I don't need this crap." F = Resentful, anxious, fearful, ashamed U = Lash out, punish others, isolate A = Become verbally abusive, feel sorry for myself R = They nag me, and I get angrier.
7. Title: Needy Little Girl Description: "I know I'm in trouble with my recovery when I start convincing myself that I just need a man to be happy again." T = "This time for sure." "He can save me." "I need this." "What's wrong with me?" F = Scared, anxious, excited, ashamed U = Escape into sex, do anything he wants, beat myself up A = Play doormat, yell at myself for how screwed up I am R = Men take advantage of me, and I keep trying to please them.	**7. Title: Damn Them to Hell** Description: "I know I'm in trouble with my recovery when I continue to blame others for all of my problems so I don't have to change." T = "What the hell." "This really sucks." "I can't stand this." "It's not my fault." F = Angry, threatened, afraid, sad U = Escape, lash out, sleep A = Escape in sleep R = People call me all concerned, but it just makes me mad.
8. Title: Custom Doormat Description: "I know I'm in trouble with my recovery when I let men take advantage of me, push me around, and then make excuses for them." T = "I deserve this." "He knows what's best for me." "What the hell's wrong with me?" F = Angry, ashamed, afraid, frustrated U = Try harder, do whatever they want, escape A = Call my dad, do whatever the men want even if it betrays my values R = Men are disgusted with me, dad wants to rescue me, and I feel like a loser.	**8. Title: Sleepy Sleep Time** Description: "I know I'm in trouble with my recovery when I keep crawling into bed to avoid thinking about my problems because they hurt too much." T = "I deserve this." "I'm taking care of myself." "It's none of their business." "I can't deal with this." F = Agitated, anxious, angry, paranoid U = Escape, hide from others A = Stay in bed, start obsessing that others are out to get me R = Avoid others because I think they want to get me in trouble.

9. Title: Fallen Angel Description: "I know I'm in trouble with my recovery when I go against my values and indulge in self-destructive behaviors and disappoint those who love me." T = "I'm a whore." "I don't deserve love." "I'm a loser." "Life sucks." F = Angry, ashamed, afraid, lonely, sad U = Escape, call dad, numb out, give up A = Obsess about how screwed up I am, call my dad and complain R = Dad insists I come over, men leave me, friends and family are ashamed of me.	**9. Title: What Now?** Description: "I know I'm in trouble with my recovery when I start believing that everyone is out to get me and project that anything that can go wrong will." T = "I'm out of here." "Help!" "Why me?" "I don't deserve this." F = Afraid, angry, frustrated, lonely U = Go shopping, act out sexually, gamble A = Spend too much, gamble and lose, hire hookers R = Others condemn me or feel sorry or afraid for me, but I justify my behaviors.
10. Title: Safe Haven, My Ass Description: "I know I'm in trouble with my recovery when I convince myself going to visit my dad is a good idea." T = "Dad loves me." "I won't be tempted." "I can handle this." "Nobody else cares." F = Excited, guilty, sad, lonely, frustrated U = Stuff my feelings, con dad, go to the bathroom A = Lie to dad, reluctantly avoid the bath-room R = Dad wants to comfort me and offers some of his Xanax.	**10. Title: Little Tin God** Description: "I know I'm in trouble with my recovery when I mistakenly believe I deserve to do what I want, and I'm the only one who knows what's best for me." T = "It's none of their business." "I deserve to have fun." "I need this." "Screw them." F = Angry, resentful, ashamed, guilty U = Escape, keep acting out A = Keep distracting myself, lie to myself R = Others are frustrated with me or afraid for me, but I won't let it in.
11. Title: Daddy Dearest Description: "I know I'm in trouble with my recovery when I convince myself it's safe to stay with dad for awhile, but I start obsessing about his medicine cabinet." T = "I need daddy." "He'll help me." "Life sucks." "Screw it." "Why not?" F = Afraid, angry with myself, lonely, ashamed U = Take meds from dad, con dad, run away, beat myself up A = Complain to dad, put myself down, re-luctantly refuse Xanax R = Dad feels sorry for me, and I feel worse; other people pull away.	**11. Title: How Low Can I Go** Description: "I know I'm in trouble with my recovery when I won't see the problems I keep creating for myself, and I keep spiraling lower and lower." T = "What am I going to do?" "Everything's fine." "What's the problem?" "I'm OK." F = Agitated, anxious, afraid, angry U = Shut down, isolate A = Avoid others, stuff my feelings, hate myself R = Since I won't let anyone near me, I don't know how they feel at this point.

12. Title: Doomed Description: "I know I'm in trouble with my recovery when I start telling myself nobody ever will be able to help me, and I'm hopeless, so why try." T = "I'm doomed." "Why go on?" "What's wrong with me?" "I'm a mess." F = Afraid, ashamed, angry, lonely, depressed, sad, frustrated U = Buy some wine; take Xanax A = Run home and lock myself in my room R = Dad is disappointed and mad at me.	**12. Title: Shame, Shame, Shame** Description: "I know I'm in trouble with my recovery when I finally realize how bad I'm really screwing up, and now I really want to escape." T = "What did I do?" "I'm such a screwup." "Oh my god." "I'm such a loser." F = Ashamed, guilty, afraid, lonely, angry U = Hide, escape, run away A = Continue to hide out R = Others are sending me panic messages of concern, but I don't believe I deserve help at this point.
13. Title: Spinning Out of Control Description: "I know I'm in trouble with my recovery when my brain is racing, and I can't turn off the addict voice wanting wine and Xanax." T = "No one will know." "I'll just drink one." "I'll just take one Xanax." "I deserve this." F = Afraid, excited, lonely, angry, exhausted U = Drink a glass of wine, take a Xanax A = I take one Xanax. R = I'm ashamed and feel like a loser once again.	**13. Title: Bad to the Bone** Description: "I know I'm in trouble with my recovery when I go back to hanging out with dangerous people and continue to do things that hurt those I love." T = "They like me." "They're my real friends." "This is more like it." "Finally!" F = Excited, strong, anxious, angry U = Stop going to meetings, go to the old hangouts A = I quit my meetings and hang out in the old places R = My old gang is congratulating me on finally getting "real"; my recovery friends are afraid for me.
14. Title: Bad Choices Description: "I know I'm in trouble with my recovery when I give in to my addict voice and start using again and am "surprised" when I'm in trouble yet again." T = "Using is good for me." "It won't be that bad." "I can handle this." "Recovery sucks." F = Angry, ashamed, disappointed, afraid, excited U = Get some wine to go with my pills A = Start drinking with the pills R = End up in the ER from an overdose	**14. Title: Recovery Sucks** Description: "I know I'm in trouble with my recovery when I see only the problems with being sober and continue glamorizing my old ways." T = "Recovery sucks." "I don't need AA." "They're losers." "I want to have fun." "I deserve this." F = Excited, happy, angry, frustrated U = Drink and use, act out, gamble A = Gamble and have sex R = Family and friends are really afraid and disgusted with me.

	15. Title: Magical Thinking Description: "I know I'm in trouble with my recovery when I convince myself that drinking and dope are what are best for me and will help me solve my problems." T = "I deserve this." "I won't get in trouble." "I can handle it this time." "No one will find out." "I can do this." F = Excited, anxious, happy, ashamed, and afraid, but stuff that U = Drink and use drugs A = Drink and use drugs R = Get arrested for a DUI and under the influence and possession of a controlled substance

After going through the directions above, Jill and Phil were able to get their cards into the final sequence you just reviewed. As you may have noticed they did keep many of their original cards, but most were modified. Now they have a sequence that shows how they became dysfunctional in their recovery and what happened to convince them that drinking or using was the solution.

Please review their examples and then go over the directions above again. Make sure you create a tight sequence of cards that demonstrate how you went from stable recovery to drinking or using other drugs. Don't forget to number your cards in case they get disorganized.

This exercise ends here.

Exercise No. 7: Identifying Three Critical-Warning Signs (CWS)

Now you need to select three (3) key or *critical-warning signs*. Critical-warning signs can alert you that you're moving toward relapse and give you a chance to stop the relapse process before it gets too strong. These are warning signs that:

1. You'll easily recognize, even if you're upset or angry (so they shouldn't be hot responses).
2. Happen early enough for you to take positive action to intervene (interrupt the process).
3. You're willing to deal with to avoid relapse.

To identify your critical-warning signs, you can:

1. Look at your final warning sign sequence and identify the warning signs that start early in the relapse process—ones that you'll be able to recognize easily and do something about.
2. Look at the warning signs you've identified as possible critical-warning signs. Pick the three that fit the description of a critical-warning sign above. Write the letters CWS in the upper-right-hand corner of each.
3. Make sure the cards for each of these warning signs are complete (i.e. has a title, a description, a thought, feeling urge and action statement). If any is missing or not clear, rewrite it.

Now, take each Critical-Warning Sign Card and review what it says. Then put the card aside and answer the following questions for each Critical-Warning Sign. After you answer the questions without referring to the card, review the card again and see if anything new or different came out. If you need to, rewrite the critical warning sign cards to make them more accurate, concrete, and specific.

Exercise 7—Part A: Completing Critical-Warning Sign No. 1

1. What is the title of this critical-warning sign?

   ____

2. Why did you select this card as a critical-warning sign?

   ____

   ____

3. Read the description statement and make sure you understand what it means.
4. Put the card aside for a moment and tell me, in other words, what the description means to you.

   ____

   ____

   ____

5. What do you tend to *think* when you experience this warning sign?

   ____

   ____

6. What do you tend to *feel* when you experience this warning sign?

7. What do you *have an urge to do* when you experience this warning sign?

8. What do you *actually do* when you experience this warning sign?

9. Can you see it is possible to put a space between the urge and action and fill that space with a conscious decision to do something different?

   ❑ Yes ❑ No ❑ Unsure Please explain:

10. How do people react to what you usually do when you experience this warning sign?

Exercise 7—Part B: Completing Critical-Warning Sign No. 2

1. What is the title of this critical-warning sign?

2. Why did you select this card as a critical-warning sign?

3. Read the description statement and make sure you understand what it means.
4. Put the card aside for a moment and tell me, in other words, what the description means to you.

5. What do you tend to *think* when you experience this warning sign?

6. What do you tend to *feel* when you experience this warning sign?

7. What do you *have an urge to do* when you experience this warning sign?

____

____

8. What do you *actually do* when you experience this warning sign?

____

____

9. Can you see it is possible to put a space between the urge and action and fill that space with a conscious decision to do something different?

   ❑ Yes ❑ No ❑ Unsure Please explain:

____

____

10. How do people react to what you usually do when you experience this warning sign?

____

Exercise 7—Part C: Completing Critical-Warning Sign No. 3

1. What is the title of this critical-warning sign?

____

2. Why did you select this card as a critical-warning sign?

____

____

3. Read the description statement and make sure you understand what it means.
4. Put the card aside for a moment and tell me, in other words, what the description means to you.

____

____

____

5. What do you tend to *think* when you experience this warning sign?

____

____

6. What do you tend to *feel* when you experience this warning sign?

____

____

7. What do you *have an urge to do* when you experience this warning sign?

____

____

8. What do you *actually do* when you experience this warning sign?

____

____

9. Can you see it is possible to put a space between the urge and action and fill that space with a conscious decision to do something different?

❑ Yes ❑ No ❑ Unsure Please explain:

____

____

10. How do people react to what you usually do when you experience this warning sign?

This exercise stops here.
Go to the next page to start the TFUAR Analysis Process.

Exercise No. 8: TFUAR Analysis—Managing Thoughts

Exercise 8—Part A: Understanding the TFUAR Sequence

It is important to learn to analyze your critical-warning signs by identifying the thoughts, feelings, urges, actions, and reactions (TFUARs) related to managing the warning signs in a way that leads to becoming dysfunctional in recovery or even relapsing.

The premise here is:

- Thoughts cause feelings.
- Thoughts and feelings cause urges.
- Urges plus decisions cause actions.
- Actions cause reactions from other people.

Making Distinctions:

- Many people have difficulty separating TFUARs…
- They can't distinguish thoughts from feelings. They tend to believe they can think anything they want, and it won't affect their feelings.
- They can't distinguish feelings from urges. They believe each feeling carries a specific urge. They don't realize they can experience a feeling, sit still, and breathe into the feeling, and it can dissipate without being acted out.
- They can't distinguish urges from actions. *Impulse control* lives in the space between the urge and the action. This space needs to be expanded (pause and notice the urge but do nothing); and then filled with *reflection* (what do I have an urge to do? What has happened when I have done similar things in the past? What is likely to happen if I do that now?) and *decision* (What do I choose to do? I know I will be responsible for the action and its consequences.).
- They can't distinguish action from social reaction. They tend to believe people respond to them for no reason at all. They don't link the responses of others to the behavior they use with others.

Irresponsible Thinking:
An irrational way of thinking that causes unnecessary emotional pain.

Irresponsible (Acting Out) Behavior:

A way of acting or behaving that causes unnecessary problems.

Addictive Thinking:
An irrational way of thinking that convinces people that alcohol and drug use is an effective way to manage the pain and problems caused by irresponsible thinking and behavior.

Emotional Consequence of Thought and Actions:
All thoughts and behaviors have logical consequences. Rational thinking allows people to deal with life without experiencing unnecessary emotional pain. Responsible behavior allows people to conduct their lives and solve their problems without producing unnecessary complications for themselves or others.

Deferred Gratification:
Deferred gratification is the ability to feel uncomfortable or to hurt now in order to gain a benefit or to feel better in the future. People who use deferred gratification *think and act better first to feel better later*.

Instant Gratification:
Instant gratification is the desire to feel better now, even if it means you will hurt worse in the future. People seeking instant gratification want to do something—anything—that instantly will make them feel better: *They want to feel better without having to think better or act better first*. This results in a quick-fix mentality. They focus upon feeling good all of the time, instead of living according to a responsible set of principles that will make their life work well. People seeking instant gratification are overly focused upon feeling good. They tend to place feeling good above all other priorities. This often is based on the mistaken belief that *"If I feel better, I will be better, and my life will be better!"*

Challenging Addictive and Irresponsible Thoughts:
The following way of thinking can challenge the tendency to seek instant gratification: The healthy goal is to live a good life regardless of how it feels at the moment. Feelings change; effective principles don't. Sober and responsible people live a life based on principles, not feelings. Instant gratification provides what looks like an easy way out. The problem is that this easy way out becomes a trap. Once trapped in a conditioned pattern of instant gratification you will feel cravings when you attempt to break the pattern. But once the pattern is broken, the urges disappear because the long-term beneficial consequences of responsible living kick in.

Exercise 8—Part B: Thought Management for the First Critical-Warning Sign

1. Look at the Warning Sign Identification Card for the critical-warning sign you are learning to manage and fill in the information requested below.

   A. **Title:** ______________________________

   B. **Description:** "I know I'm in trouble with my recovery when…"

   ____

   ____

   C. **Thought Statement:** "When I experience this warning sign I tend to think…"

   ____

   ____

2. What are three thoughts that can cause you to manage this warning sign in a way that makes things worse instead of better?

   Thought No. 1: ______________________________

   ____

   What is another way of thinking that would be more helpful?

   ____

   ____

   Thought No. 2: ______________________________

   ____

   What is another way of thinking that would be more helpful?

   ____

   ____

Thought No. 3: ______________________________

____

What is another way of thinking that would be more helpful?

____

____

Exercise 8—Part C: Thought Management for the Second Critical-Warning Sign

1. Look at the Warning Sign Identification Card for the critical warning sign you are learning to manage and fill in the information requested below.

   A. **Title:** ______________________________

   B. **Description:** "I know I'm in trouble with my recovery when…"

   ____

   ____

   C. **Thought Statement:** "When I experience this warning sign I tend to think…"

   ____

   ____

2. What are three thoughts that can cause you to manage this warning sign in a way that makes things worse instead of better?

   Thought No. 1: ______________________________

   ____

   What is another way of thinking that would be more helpful?

   ____

   ____

   Thought No. 2: ______________________________

   ____

   What is another way of thinking that would be more helpful?

   ____

   ____

   Thought No. 3: ______________________________

   ____

   What is another way of thinking that would be more helpful?

   ____

   ____

Exercise 8—Part D: Thought Management for the Third Critical-Warning Sign

1. Look at the Warning Sign Identification Card for the critical warning sign you are learning to manage and fill in the information requested below.

   A. **Title:** ______________________________

   B. **Description:** "I know that I'm in trouble with my recovery when …"

   ____

   ____

   C. **Thought Statement:** "When I am experiencing this warning sign I tend to think …"

   ____

   ____

2. What are three thoughts that can cause you to manage this warning sign in a way that makes things worse instead of better?

   Thought No. 1: ______________________________

   ____

   What is another way of thinking that would be more helpful?

   ____

   ____

   Thought No. 2: ______________________________

   ____

   What is another way of thinking that would be more helpful?

   ____

   ____

   Thought No. 3: ______________________________

   ____

   What is another way of thinking that would be more helpful?

   ____

   ____

Go to the next page to learn how to handle the feelings related to these three warning signs.

Exercise No. 9: TFUAR Analysis—Managing Feelings

Exercise 9—Part A: Feeling Management for the First Critical-Warning Sign

1. Look at the Warning Sign Identification Card for the critical-warning sign you are learning to manage and fill in the information requested below.

   A. **Title:** ______________________________

   B. **Description:** "I know I'm in trouble with my recovery when..."

   ____

   ____

   C. **Feeling Statement:** "When I experience this warning sign I tend to feel..."

   ____

   ____

2. **Feeling Checklist:** Review the feeling list below and check all of the feelings you experience when this warning sign is turned on. Answer the two clarifying questions about each warning sign you check.

   When you experience this warning sign, do you tend to feel...

   ❑ *Strong* or ❑ *Weak*? How intense is the feeling? (0–10) _____

   Why do you rate it this way? ______________________________

   ❑ *Angry* or ❑ *Caring*? How intense is the feeling? (0–10) _____

   Why do you rate it this way? ______________________________

   ❑ *Happy* or ❑ *Sad*? How intense is the feeling? (0–10) _____

   Why do you rate it this way? ______________________________

   ❑ *Safe* or ❑ *Threatened*? How intense is the feeling? (0–10) ____

   Why do you rate it this way? ______________________________

   ❑ *Fulfilled* or ❑ *Frustrated*? How intense is the feeling? (0–10) ____

   Why do you rate it this way? ______________________________

   ❑ *Proud* or ❑ *Shamed*? How intense is the feeling? (0–10) ____

   Why do you rate it this way? ______________________________

   ❑ *Lonely* or ❑ *Connected*? How intense is the feeling? (0–10) ____

   Why do you rate it this way? ______________________________

   ❑ *Peaceful* or ❑ *Agitated*? How intense is the feeling? (0–10) ____

   Why do you rate it this way? ______________________________

3. **Three Strongest Feelings:** What are the three strongest feelings you have when this warning sign is turned on?

   Feeling No. 1: ______________________________

   Why did you choose this feeling? ______________________________

   Feeling No. 2: ______________________________

Why did you choose this feeling? ______________________________

Feeling No. 3: ______________________________

Why did you choose this feeling? ______________________________

4. **Feeling that You Want To Learn to Manage:** Review the three feelings you identified above and select the feeling you want to learn to manage more effectively.

____

A. What are you *thinking* that makes you feel this way?

____

____

B. What is another way of *thinking* that would help you manage this feeling better?

____

____

C. What are you *doing* that makes you feel this way?

____

____

D. What is another thing that you could be *doing* to manage this feeling better?

____

____

5. What can you do to recognize this feeling as soon as it occurs?

____

____

Here are some things other people have found helpful:
A. Plan ahead and learn to anticipate situations that are likely to cause this feeling.
B. Stay centered and aware of the rise and fall of inner feelings.
C. Take a deep breath and notice when I am starting to have this feeling.

6. What can you do to clarify what you are feeling?

____

____

Here are some things other people have found helpful:
A. Find words that describe what I'm feeling (using the feeling list if needed).
B. Rate the intensity of my feelings using a 10-point scale.
C. Consciously acknowledge the feeling and its intensity by saying to myself, "Right now I'm feeling ______________, and it's OK to feel this way."

7. Who can you talk to about the feeling to help you to manage it better?

____

____

Here are some things other people have found helpful:

A. Ask my therapist, therapy group, or recovery support group about who could talk with me about this feeling.
B. Call that person as soon as I recognize I'm having the feeling.
C. Talk about what I am feeling with my therapist, therapy group, or at a twelve-step meeting.

8. What can you do to figure out what is causing you to feel this way?

____

____

Here are some things other people have found helpful:

A. Identify *what I'm thinking* that's making me feel this way and ask myself, "How can I change my thinking in a way that will make me feel better?"
B. Identify *what I'm doing* that's making me feel this way and ask myself, "How can I change what I'm doing in a way that will make me feel better?"
C. Recognize the *mistaken beliefs*, irrational mandates, and injunctions that are triggering the feeling.

9. What can you do to stop yourself from automatically reacting to this feeling without thinking it through?

____

____

Here are some things other people have found helpful:

A. Call a time-out before the feeling becomes unmanageable.
B. Use an immediate relaxation technique to bring down the intensity of the feeling.
C. Consciously stop the urge to react automatically to the feeling without thinking it through.
D. Recognize and resist urges that create problems, hurt myself, or hurt other people in an attempt to make myself feel better.
E. Recognize my resistance to doing things that would help me or my situation, and *motivate myself* to do those things despite the resistance.

Exercise 9—Part B: Feeling Management for the Second Critical-Warning Sign

1. Look at the Warning Sign Identification Card for the critical-warning sign you are learning to manage and fill in the information requested below.

   A. **Title:** ____________________

   B. **Description:** "I know I'm in trouble with my recovery when…"

   ____

   ____

   C. **Feeling Statement:** "When I experience this warning sign I tend to feel…"

   ____

   ____

2. **Feeling Checklist:** Review the feeling list below and check all feelings you experience when this warning sign is turned on. Answer the two clarifying questions about each warning sign that you check.

   When you experience this warning sign do you tend to feel...

   ❑ *Strong* or ❑ *Weak*? How intense is the feeling? (0–10) _____

   Why do you rate it this way? ____________________

   ❑ *Angry* or ❑ *Caring*? How intense is the feeling? (0–10) _____

   Why do you rate it this way? ____________________

   ❑ *Happy* or ❑ *Sad*? How intense is the feeling? (0–10) _____

   Why do you rate it this way? ____________________

   ❑ *Safe* or ❑ *Threatened*? How intense is the feeling? (0–10) ____

   Why do you rate it this way? ____________________

   ❑ *Fulfilled* or ❑ *Frustrated*? How intense is the feeling? (0–10) ____

   Why do you rate it this way? ____________________

   ❑ *Proud* or ❑ *Shamed*? How intense is the feeling? (0–10) ____

   Why do you rate it this way? ____________________

   ❑ *Lonely* or ❑ *Connected*? How intense is the feeling? (0–10) ____

   Why do you rate it this way? ____________________

   ❑ *Peaceful* or ❑ *Agitated*? How intense is the feeling? (0–10) ____

   Why do you rate it this way? ____________________

3. **Three Strongest Feelings:** What are the three strongest feelings you have when this warning sign is turned on?

   Feeling No. 1: ____________________

   Why did you choose this feeling? ____________________

   Feeling No. 2: ____________________

Why did you choose this feeling? ________________________________

Feeling No. 3: ________________________________

Why did you choose this feeling? ________________________________

4. **Feeling that You Want to Learn to Manage:** Review the three feelings you identified above and select the feeling you want to learn to manage more effectively.

____

A. What are you *thinking* that makes you feel this way?

____

____

B. What is another way of *thinking* that would help you manage this feeling better?

____

____

C. What are you *doing* that makes you feel this way?

____

____

D. What is another thing that you could be *doing* to manage this feeling better?

____

____

5. What can you do to recognize this feeling as soon as it occurs?

____

____

> Here are some things other people have found helpful:
> A. Plan ahead and learn to anticipate situations likely to cause this feeling.
> B. Stay centered and aware of the rise and fall of inner feelings.
> C. Take a deep breath and notice when I am starting to have this feeling.

6. What can you do to clarify what you are feeling?

____

____

> Here are some things that other people have found helpful:
> A. Find words that describe what I'm feeling (using the feeling list if needed).
> B. Rate the intensity of my feelings using a ten-point scale.
> C. Consciously acknowledge the feeling and its intensity by saying to myself, "Right now I'm feeling ____________, and it's OK to feel this way."

7. Who can you talk to about the feeling to help you to manage it better?

____

____

Here are some things other people have found helpful:

A. Ask my therapist, therapy group, or recovery support group about who could talk with me about this feeling.
B. Call that person as soon as I recognize I'm having the feeling.
C. Talk about what I am feeling with my therapist, therapy group, or at a twelve-step meeting.

8. What can you do to figure out what is causing you to feel this way?

____

____

Here are some things other people have found helpful:

A. Identify *what I'm thinking* that makes me feel this way and ask myself, "How can I change my thinking in a way that will make me feel better?"
B. Identify *what I'm doing* that makes me feel this way and ask myself, "How can I change what I'm doing in a way that will make me feel better?"
C. Recognize the *mistaken beliefs*, irrational mandates, and injunctions that trigger the feeling.

9. What can you do to stop yourself from automatically reacting to this feeling without thinking it through?

____

____

Here are some things other people have found helpful:

A. Call a time-out before the feeling becomes unmanageable.
B. Use an immediate relaxation technique to bring down the intensity of the feeling.
C. Consciously stop the urge to react automatically to the feeling without thinking it through.
D. Recognize and resist urges that create problems, hurt myself, or hurt other people in an attempt to make myself feel better.
E. Recognize my resistance to doing things that would help me or my situation, and *motivate myself* to do those things despite the resistance.

Exercise 9—Part C: Feeling Management for the Third Critical-Warning Sign

1. Look at the Warning Sign Identification Card for the critical-warning sign you are learning to manage and fill in the information requested below.

   A. **Title:** ______________________________

   B. **Description:** "I know I'm in trouble with my recovery when…"

   ____

   ____

   C. **Feeling Statement:** "When I experience this warning sign I tend to feel…"

   ____

   ____

2. **Feeling Checklist:** Review the feeling list below and check all feelings you experience when this warning sign is turned on. Answer the two clarifying questions about each warning sign you check.

   When you experience this warning sign do you tend to feel...

   ❑ *Strong* or ❑ *Weak*? How intense is the feeling? (0–10) _____

   Why do you rate it this way? ______________________________

   ❑ *Angry* or ❑ *Caring*? How intense is the feeling? (0–10) _____

   Why do you rate it this way? ______________________________

   ❑ *Happy* or ❑ *Sad*? How intense is the feeling? (0–10) _____

   Why do you rate it this way? ______________________________

   ❑ *Safe* or ❑ *Threatened*? How intense is the feeling? (0–10) ____

   Why do you rate it this way? ______________________________

   ❑ *Fulfilled* or ❑ *Frustrated*? How intense is the feeling? (0–10) ____

   Why do you rate it this way? ______________________________

   ❑ *Proud* or ❑ *Shamed*? How intense is the feeling? (0–10) ____

   Why do you rate it this way? ______________________________

   ❑ *Lonely* or ❑ *Connected*? How intense is the feeling? (0–10) ____

   Why do you rate it this way? ______________________________

   ❑ *Peaceful* or ❑ *Agitated*? How intense is the feeling? (0–10) ____

   Why do you rate it this way? ______________________________

3. **Three Strongest Feelings:** What are the three strongest feelings you have when this warning sign is turned on?

   Feeling No. 1: ______________________________

   Why did you choose this feeling? ______________________________

   Feeling No. 2: ______________________________

Why did you choose this feeling? ______________________________

Feeling No. 3: ______________________________

Why did you choose this feeling? ______________________________

4. **Feeling that You Want To Learn to Manage:** Review the three feelings you identified above and select the feeling you want to learn to manage more effectively.

____

A. What are you *thinking* that makes you feel this way?

____

____

B. What is another way of *thinking* that would help you manage this feeling better?

____

____

C. What are you *doing* that makes you feel this way?

____

____

D. What is another thing you could be *doing* to manage this feeling better?

____

____

5. What can you do to recognize this feeling as soon as it occurs?

____

____

Here are some things other people have found helpful:
A. Plan ahead and learn to anticipate situations likely to cause this feeling.
B. Stay centered and aware of the rise and fall of inner feelings.
C. Take a deep breath and notice when I am starting to have this feeling.

6. What can you do to clarify what you are feeling?

____

____

Here are some things other people have found helpful:
A. Find words that describe what I'm feeling (using the feeling list if needed).
B. Rate the intensity of my feelings using a ten-point scale.
C. Consciously acknowledge the feeling and its intensity by saying to myself, "Right now I'm feeling ____________, and it's OK to feel this way."

7. Who can you talk to about the feeling to help you manage it better?

____

____

Here are some things other people have found helpful:
A. Ask my therapist, therapy group, or recovery support group about who could talk with me about this feeling.
B. Call that person as soon as I recognize I'm having the feeling.
C. Talk about what I am feeling with my therapist, therapy group, or at a twelve-step meeting.

8. What can you do to figure out what is causing you to feel this way?

____

____

Here are some things other people have found helpful:
A. Identify *what I'm thinking* that makes me feel this way and ask myself, "How can I change my thinking in a way that will make me feel better?"
B. Identify *what I'm doing* that makes me feel this way and ask myself, "How can I change what I'm doing in a way that will make me feel better?"
C. Recognize the *mistaken beliefs,* irrational mandates, and injunctions that trigger the feeling.

9. What can you do to stop yourself from automatically reacting to this feeling without thinking it through?

____

____

Here are some things other people have found helpful:
A. Call a time-out before the feeling becomes unmanageable,
B. Use an immediate relaxation technique to bring down the intensity of the feeling,
C. Consciously stop the urge to react automatically to the feeling without thinking it through.
D. Recognize and resist urges that create problems, hurt myself, or hurt other people in an attempt to make myself feel better.
E. Recognize my resistance to doing things that would help me or my situation, and *motivate myself* to do those things despite the resistance.

This exercise ends here.
Go to the next page to learn how to handle the urges related to the three critical-warning signs.

Exercise No. 10: TFUAR Analysis—Managing Urges

Exercise 10—Part A: Managing Urges for the First Critical-Warning Sign

1. Look at the Warning Sign Identification Card for the critical-warning sign you are learning to manage and fill in the information requested below.

   A. **Title:** ____________________

   B. **Description:** "I know I'm in trouble with my recovery when…"

   ____

   ____

   C. **Urge Statement:** When I am experiencing this warning sign I have an urge to…

   ____

   ____

2. **Self-destructive Urges:** When you experience this warning sign, what do you have an urge to do that would make things worse in the long run?

   ____

   ____

   ____

   A. Notice that *a part of you wants to use self-destructive behavior* that will make things worse. Tell me about that part of you.

   ____

   ____

   B. Notice that *a part of you wants to resist the urge to use this self-destructive behavior* and wants to find a more effective way of managing this warning sign. Tell me about that part of you.

   ____

   ____

3. **Constructive Urges:** If you wanted to manage this warning sign more effectively, what part of yourself do you need to listen to and why?

   ____

   ____

Exercise 10—Part B: Managing Urges for the Second Critical-Warning Sign

1. Look at the Warning Sign Identification Card for the critical-warning sign you are learning to manage and fill in the information requested below.

   A. **Title:** ____________________

   B. **Description:** "I know I'm in trouble with my recovery when…"

   ____

   ____

C. **Urge Statement:** "When I experience this warning sign I have an urge to…"

____

____

2. **Self-destructive Urges:** When you experience this warning sign, what do you have an urge to do that would make things worse in the long run?

____

____

____

A. Notice that *a part of you wants to use self-destructive behavior* that will make things worse. Tell me about that part of you.

____

____

B. Notice that *a part of you wants to resist the urge to use this self-destructive behavior* and wants to find a more effective way of managing this warning sign? Tell me about that part of you.

____

____

3. **Constructive Urges:** If you wanted to manage this warning sign more effectively, what part of yourself do you need to listen to and why?

____

____

Exercise 10—Part C: Managing Urges for the Third Critical-Warning Sign

1. Look at the Warning Sign Identification Card for the critical-warning sign you are learning to manage and fill in the information requested below.

A. **Title:** ____

B. **Description:** "I know I'm in trouble with my recovery when…"

____

____

C. **Urge Statement:** "When I experience this warning sign I have an urge to…"

____

____

2. **Self-destructive Urges:** When you experience this warning sign, what do you have an urge to do that would make things worse in the long run?

____

____

____

A. Notice that *a part of you wants to use self-destructive behavior* that will make things worse. Tell me about that part of you.

____

____

B. Notice that *a part of you wants to resist the urge to use this self-destructive behavior* and wants to find a more-effective way of managing this warning sign. Tell me about that part of you.

____

____

3. **Constructive Urges:** If you wanted to manage this warning sign more effectively, what part of yourself do you need to listen to and why?

____

____

This exercise ends here.
Go to the next page to learn how to manage the actions (things that you do) that are related to your warning signs.

Exercise No. 11: TFUAR Analysis—Managing Actions

Exercise 11—Part A: Managing Actions for the First Critical-Warning Sign

1. Look at the Warning Sign Identification Card for the critical-warning sign you are learning to manage and fill in the information requested below.

   A. **Title:** ____________________

   B. **Description:** "I know I'm in trouble with my recovery when…"

   ____

   ____

   C. **Action Statement:** "When I experience this warning sign, what I actually do is…"

   ____

   ____

2. **Self-defeating Behavior Checklist:** Keeping this warning sign in mind, read the following checklist of *self-defeating behaviors* that can be used to manage this warning sign in a way that makes things worse. Check the behaviors you are most likely to use.

   1. **Procrastinating:** "I put off dealing with the warning sign by…"
      - ❑ a) finding excuses or reasons for not doing it now;
      - ❑ b) getting too busy with other things to do it now;
      - ❑ c) seeing other things as more important;
      - ❑ d) convincing myself that nothing is wrong;
      - ❑ e) convincing myself that I'm too weak and helpless.
   2. **Mismanaging:** I try to manage the warning sign by using old, self-defeating behaviors, and I make things worse by:
      - ❑ a) reacting without thinking it through;
      - ❑ b) trying to handle it by myself without asking for help;
      - ❑ c) feeling helpless and expecting others to do it for me;
      - ❑ d) constantly changing my mind and not sticking to a plan;
      - ❑ e) detaching from the situation so it doesn't bother me;
      - ❑ f) getting scared and using my fear as an excuse.

3. What are the three self-defeating behaviors you tend to use when trying to manage this warning sign? (You can use the self-defeating behaviors on your warning sign card and on the list above as a starting point, but it is important to write the descriptions in your own words.)

   A. **Self-defeating behavior No. 1:** ____________________

   ____

   Why did you choose this behavior? ____________________

   ____

B. **Self-defeating behavior No. 2:** ____________________

____

Why did you choose this behavior? ____________________

____

C. **Self-defeating behavior No. 3:** ____________________

____

Why did you choose this behavior? ____________________

____

4. **Self-defeating Behavior You Want to Learn to Manage:** Select the self-defeating behavior you want to learn to manage more effectively.

____

____

A. What makes you want to use this self-defeating behavior?

____

____

B. What do you want to accomplish by using it?

____

____

C. Does this self-defeating behavior get you what you want?

❑ Yes ❑ No ❑ Unsure Why did you answer this way?

____

____

D. When you use this self-defeating behavior, how do other people usually react to you?

____

____

E. Does the way that other people react to you make it harder or easier to manage this warning sign effectively?

❑ Harder ❑ Easier ❑ Unsure Why did you answer this way?

____

____

F. How could other people react to you in a way that would help you stay away from alcohol or drugs?

____

____

5. What is another way of behaving that could help you manage this situation more effectively?

A. How can you motivate yourself to manage this warning sign in this new and more-effective way?

B. What could you invite other people to do to help you deal more effectively with this warning sign?

Exercise 11—Part B: Managing Actions for the Second Critical-Warning Sign

1. Look at the Warning Sign Identification Card for the critical-warning sign you are learning to manage and fill in the information requested below.

A. **Title:**

B. **Description:** "I know I'm in trouble with my recovery when…"

C. **Action Statement:** "When I experience this warning sign what I actually do is…"

2. **Self-defeating Behavior Checklist:** Keeping this warning sign in mind, read the following checklist of *self-defeating behaviors* that can be used to manage this warning sign in a way that makes things worse. Check the behaviors you are most likely to use.

1. **Procrastinating:** "I put off dealing with the warning sign by…"

❑ a) finding excuses or reasons for not doing it now;

❑ b) getting too busy with other things to do it now;

❑ c) seeing other things as more important;

❑ d) convincing myself that nothing is wrong;

❑ e) convincing myself that I'm too weak and helpless.

2. **Mismanaging:** I try to manage the warning sign by using old, self-defeating behaviors, and I make things worse by:

❑ a) reacting without thinking it through;

❑ b) trying to handle it by myself without asking for help;

- ❑ c) feeling helpless and expecting others to do it for me;
- ❑ d) constantly changing my mind and not sticking to a plan;
- ❑ e) detaching from the situation so it doesn't bother me;
- ❑ f) getting scared and using my fear as an excuse.

3. What are the three self-defeating behaviors you tend to use when trying to manage this warning sign? (You can use the self-defeating behaviors on your warning sign card and on the list above as a starting point, but it is important to write the description in your own words.)

A. **Self-defeating Behavior No. 1:** ______________________

____

____

Why did you choose this behavior? ______________________

____

B. **Self-defeating Behavior No. 2:** ______________________

____

____

Why did you choose this behavior? ______________________

____

C. **Self-defeating Behavior No. 3:** ______________________

____

____

Why did you choose this behavior? ______________________

____

4. **Self-defeating Behavior You Want to Learn to Manage:** Select the self-defeating behavior you want to learn to manage more effectively.

____

____

A. What makes you want to use this self-defeating behavior?

____

____

B. What do you want to accomplish by using it?

____

____

C. Does this self-defeating behavior get you what you want?

❑ Yes ❑ No ❑ Unsure Why did you answer this way?

____

____

D. When you use this self-defeating behavior how do other people usually react to you?

____

____

E. Does the way other people react to you make it harder or easier to manage this warning sign effectively?

❑ Harder ❑ Easier ❑ Unsure Why did you answer this way?

____

____

F. How could other people react to you in a way that would help you stay away from alcohol or drugs?

____

____

5. What is another way of acting that could help you manage this situation more effectively?

____

____

A. How can you motivate yourself to manage this warning sign in this new and more-effective way?

____

____

B. What could you invite other people to do to help you deal more effectively with this warning sign?

____

____

____

Exercise 11—Part C: Managing Actions for the Third Critical-Warning Sign

1. Look at the Warning Sign Identification Card for the critical-warning sign you are learning to manage and fill in the information requested below.

A. **Title:** ____

B. **Description:** "I know I'm in trouble with my recovery when…"

____

____

C. **Action Statement:** "When I experience this warning sign, what I actually do is…"

____

____

2. **Self-defeating Behavior Checklist:** Keeping this warning sign in mind, read the following checklist of *self-defeating behaviors* that can be used to manage this warning sign in a way that makes things worse. Check the behaviors you are most likely to use.

   1. **Procrastinating:** "I put off dealing with the warning sign by…"
      - ❑ a) finding excuses or reasons for not doing it now;
      - ❑ b) getting too busy with other things to do it now;
      - ❑ c) seeing other things as more important;
      - ❑ d) convincing myself that nothing is wrong;
      - ❑ e) convincing myself that I'm too weak and helpless.

   2. **Mismanaging:** I try to manage the warning sign by using old, self-defeating behaviors, and I make things worse by:
      - ❑ a) reacting without thinking it through;
      - ❑ b) trying to handle it by myself without asking for help;
      - ❑ c) feeling helpless and expecting others to do it for me;
      - ❑ d) constantly changing my mind and not sticking to a plan;
      - ❑ e) detaching from the situation so it doesn't bother me;
      - ❑ f) getting scared and using my fear as an excuse.

3. What are the three self-defeating behaviors you tend to use when trying to manage this warning sign? (You can use the self-defeating behaviors on your warning sign card and on the list above as a starting point, but it is important to write the descriptions in your own words.)

   A. **Self-defeating Behavior No. 1:**

   ____

   ____

   ____

   Why did you choose this behavior? ____

   ____

   B. **Self-defeating Behavior No. 2:**

   ____

   ____

   ____

   Why did you choose this behavior? ____

   ____

C. **Self-defeating Behavior No. 3:**

____

____

____

Why did you choose this behavior? ______________________________

____

4. **Self-defeating Behavior You Want to Learn to Manage:** Select the self-defeating behavior you want to learn to manage more effectively?

____

A. What makes you want to use this self-defeating behavior?

____

____

B. What do you want to accomplish by using it?

____

____

C. Does this self-defeating behavior get you what you want?

❑ Yes ❑ No ❑ Unsure Why did you answer this way?

____

____

D. When you use this self-defeating behavior how do other people usually react to you?

____

____

E. Does the way that other people react to you make it harder or easier to manage this warning sign effectively?

❑ Harder ❑ Easier ❑ Unsure Why did you answer this way?

____

____

F. How could other people react to you in a way that would help you stay away from alcohol or drugs?

____

____

5. What is another way of behaving that could help you manage this situation more effectively?

____

____

A. How can you motivate yourself to manage this warning sign in this new and more-effective way?

____

____

B. What could you invite other people to do to help you deal more effectively with this warning sign?

____

____

____

This exercise ends here.
Go to the next page to learn how to tie together everything you have learned about managing these critical-warning signs.

Exercise No. 12: Managing Personal Reactions to Critical-Warning Signs

This exercise will help you tie together everything you have learned from completing the previous four exercises. Before completing this exercise review *the previous exercises related to TFUAR management*. Take time to reflect on each answer and try to see what you really were saying in your answers. Also try to see how the answers to different questions somehow are related or connected to other answers. Then complete the questions in the table below. If you need to, you can clarify the title and descriptions of the warning signs.

Exercise 12—Part A: Managing Reactions to the First Critical-Warning Sign

1. Look at the Warning Sign Identification Card for the critical-warning sign you are learning to manage and fill in the information requested below.

   A. **Title:** ______________________________

   B. **Description:** "I know I'm in trouble with my recovery when…"

   ____

   ____

2-a. When you experience this warning sign what do you tend to think?	2-b. What is another way of thinking that will help you manage this warning sign better?
______________________________ ______________________________ ______________________________ ______________________________ ______________________________ ______________________________	______________________________ ______________________________ ______________________________ ______________________________ ______________________________ ______________________________
3-a. When you experience this warning sign what do you feel? How do you mismanage those feelings in a self-defeating way?	**3-b. What is another way to manage these feelings that will help you deal with this warning sign better?**
______________________________ ______________________________ ______________________________ ______________________________ ______________________________ ______________________________	______________________________ ______________________________ ______________________________ ______________________________ ______________________________ ______________________________

4-a. When you experience this warning sign what do you have an urge to do?	4-b. What is another way of managing this urge that will help you deal with this warning sign better?
5-a. When you experience this warning sign what do you usually do?	**5-b.** What are some other things you can do that will help you deal with this warning sign better?
6-a. When you experience this warning sign how do other people usually react?	**6-b.** How can you invite other people to react to you in a way that will help you deal with this warning sign better?

7. **Most-Important Thing Learned**: What is the most-important thing you learned by completing this exercise?

Exercise 12—Part B: Managing Reactions to the Second Critical-Warning Sign

1. Look at the Warning Sign Identification Card for the critical-warning sign you are learning to manage and fill in the information requested below.

   A. **Title:** ______________________________

   B. **Description:** "I know I'm in trouble with my recovery when…"

   ____

   ____

2-a. When you experience this warning sign what do you tend to think?	2-b. What is another way of thinking that will help you manage this warning sign better?
3-a. When you experience this warning sign what do you feel? How do you mismanage those feelings in a self-defeating way?	**3-b. What is another way to manage these feelings that will help you deal with this warning sign better?**
4-a. When you experience this warning sign what do you have an urge to do?	**4-b. What is another way of managing this urge that will help you deal with this warning sign better?**

5-a. When you experience this warning sign what do you usually do?	5-b. What are some other things you can do that will help you deal with this warning sign better?

6-a. When you experience this warning sign how do other people usually react?	6-b. How can you invite other people to react to you in a way that will help you deal with this warning sign better?

7. **Most-Important Thing Learned**: What is the most-important thing you learned by completing this exercise?

Exercise 12—Part C: Managing Reactions to the Third Critical-Warning Sign

1. Look at the Warning Sign Identification Card for the critical-warning sign you are learning to manage and fill in the information requested below.

   A. **Title:** ____________________

   B. **Description:** "I know I'm in trouble with my recovery when…"

   ____

   ____

2-a. When you experience this warning sign what do you tend to think?	2-b. What is another way of thinking that will help you manage this warning sign better?
3-a. When you experience this warning sign what do you feel? How do you mismanage those feelings in a self-defeating way?	**3-b. What is another way to manage these feelings that will help you deal with this warning sign better?**
4-a. When you experience this warning sign what do you have an urge to do?	**4-b. What is another way of managing this urge that will help you deal with this warning sign better?**

5-a. When you experience this warning sign what do you usually do?	5-b. What are some other things you can do that will help you deal with this warning sign better?
6-a. When you experience this warning sign how do other people usually react?	**6-b.** How can you invite other people to react to you in a way that will help you deal with this warning sign better?

7. **Most-Important Thing Learned**: What is the most-important thing you learned by completing this exercise?

This exercise ends here.

Exercise No. 13: Building a Recovery Program for Relapse Prevention

Exercise 13—Part A: Selecting Recovery Activities

Now that you have identified the critical-warning signs that lead from stable recovery to relapse, it is time to develop a schedule of recovery activities that can help you manage those critical-warning signs.

Recovery is like walking up and down an escalator. There is no such thing as standing still. You will need to work every day at identifying your relapse warning signs and the thoughts, feelings, and actions that drive them. You constantly must put yourself in situations that will support sober and responsible living. You consciously must use new ways of thinking, managing your feelings, and acting when you are in those situations.

At first this will be hard because your old habits have been ingrained deeply in your personality. Without a daily schedule of recovery activities, you will relapse into old ways of thinking, managing your feelings, acting, and relating to others. This will lead you to get involved in old situations and eventually cause you to relapse.

If you consistently practice the new ways of thinking, feeling, and acting by following your recovery program, the new behaviors will begin to feel comfortable. After four to six weeks of consistently following the program, most of these activities will become unconscious habits that are easy to maintain. Because these new habits are effective, your life will become more manageable, and you will find your ability to feel good about life will increase.

The following procedure will help you understand what recovery activities may be helpful. It then will help you develop an initial recovery plan, test it to be sure it deals with your critical-warning signs, and revise and strengthen it so it can be effective in preventing relapse. Finally, you will be shown how to use morning and evening inventories to keep your recovery on task.

Exercise 13—Part B: Selecting Your Initial Recovery Activities

Having a plan for each day will help you recover. People who successfully recover tend to do certain basic things. These recovery principles are proven. In AA, there is such a strong belief that they work that many people with solid recovery will say, "If you want what we have, do what we did!" and, "It works if you work it!"

However, not everyone in recovery does exactly the same things. Once you understand yourself and the basic principles of recovery and relapse prevention, you can build an effective personal program for yourself.

When people first read the following list, they tend to get defensive. "I can't do all of those things!" they say to themselves. I invite you to think about your recovery as if you were hiking in the Grand Canyon and had to jump across a ravine that is about three feet wide and 100 feet deep. It is better to jump three feet too far than risk jumping one inch too short. The same is true of recovery. It is better to plan to do a little bit more than you need to do than to risk not doing enough. In AA they say, "Half measures availed us nothing!"

The seven basic recovery activities described below are actually habits of good, healthy living. Anyone who wants to live a responsible, healthy, and fulfilling life will get in the habit of regularly doing these things. For people in recovery from chemical dependence these activities are essential. A regular schedule of these activities, designed to match your unique profile of recovery needs and relapse warning signs, is necessary for your brain to heal from the damage caused by chronic alcohol and drug poisoning.

Instructions: Read the list of recovery activities below and identify which activities you think will be helpful in your recovery, the obstacles you face in doing them on a regular basis, and your willingness to overcome those obstacles.

1. **Professional Counseling:** Your recovery will be dependent on regular attendance at recovery-education sessions, group-therapy sessions, and individual-therapy sessions. The scientific literature on treatment effectiveness clearly shows that the more time you invest in professional counseling and therapy during the first two years of recovery, the more likely you are to stay sober.

A. "Do I believe that I need to do this?"

❑ Yes ❑ Unsure ❑ No

B. "Obstacles that will prevent me from doing it are..."

____

____

C. "My plans for overcoming any obstacles are..."

____

____

D. "Will I put this on my recovery plan?"

❑ Yes ❑ Unsure ❑ No

Please explain:

____

____

2. **Self-Help Programs:** There are several self-help programs such as Alcoholics Anonymous (AA), Narcotics Anonymous (NA), and Rational Recovery that can support your efforts to live a sober and responsible life. These programs have several things in common:

- They ask you to abstain from alcohol and drugs and live a responsible life.
- They encourage you to attend meetings regularly so you can meet and develop relationships with other people living sober and responsible lives.
- They ask you to meet regularly with an established member of the group (usually called a sponsor) who will help you learn about the organization and get through the rough spots.
- They promote a program of recovery (often in the form of steps or structured exercises that you work on outside meetings) that focuses upon techniques for changing your thinking, emotional management, and behavior. Scientific research shows that the more committed and actively involved you are in self-help groups during the first two years of recovery, the greater your ability to avoid relapse.

A. "Do I believe I need to do this?" ❑ Yes ❑ Unsure ❑ No

B. "Obstacles that will prevent me from doing it are..."

____

____

C. "My plans for overcoming any obstacles are..."

D. "Will I put this on my recovery plan?" ❑ Yes ❑ Unsure ❑ No

Please explain:

3. **Proper Diet:** What you eat can affect how you think, feel, and act. Many chemically dependent people find they feel better if they eat three well-balanced meals a day, use vitamin and amino-acid supplements, avoid eating sugar and foods made with white flour, and cut back or stop smoking cigarettes and drinking caffeinated beverages such as coffee and colas. Recovering people who don't follow these simple principles of healthy diet and meal planning tend to feel anxious and depressed, have strong and violent mood swings, feel constantly angry and resentful, periodically experience powerful cravings, and are more likely to relapse. Those who follow a proper diet feel better and have lower relapse rates.

A. "Do I believe that I need to do this?" ❑ Yes ❑ Unsure ❑ No

B. "Obstacles that will prevent me from doing it are..."

C. "My plans for overcoming any obstacles are..."

D. "Will I put this on my recovery plan?" ❑ Yes ❑ Unsure ❑ No

Please explain:

4. **Exercise Program:** Doing 30 minutes of aerobic exercise each day will help your brain recover and help you feel better about yourself. Fast walking, jogging, swimming, or aerobics classes all help. It also helps to do strength-building exercises (such as weight lifting) and flexibility exercises (such as stretching) in addition to the aerobic exercise.

A. "Do I believe I need to do this?" ❑ Yes ❑ Unsure ❑ No

B. "Obstacles that will prevent me from doing it are..."

C. "My plans for overcoming any obstacles are..."

D. "Will I put this on my recovery plan?" ❑ Yes ❑ Unsure ❑ No

Please explain:

____

____

5. **Stress-Management Program:** Stress is a major cause of relapse. Recovering people who learn to manage stress without using self-defeating behaviors stay in recovery. Those who don't learn to manage stress tend to relapse. Stress management involves learning relaxation exercises and taking quiet time on a daily basis to relax. It also involves avoiding long hours of working and taking time for recreation and relaxation.

A. "Do I believe I need to do this?" ❑ Yes ❑ Unsure ❑ No

B. "Obstacles that will prevent me from doing it are…"

____

____

C. "My plans for overcoming any obstacles are…"

____

____

D. "Will I put this on my recovery plan?" ❑ Yes ❑ Unsure ❑ No

Please explain:

____

____

6. **Spiritual-Development Program:** Human beings have both a physical self (based on the health of our brains and body) and a non-physical self (based on the health of our value systems and spiritual lives). Most recovering people find they need to invest regular time in developing themselves spiritually (in other words, exercising the non-physical aspects of who they are). Twelve-step programs such as AA provide an excellent aid for spiritual recovery, as do many communities of faith and spirituality. At the heart of any spiritual program are three activities: (1) fellowship, when you talk with people who use similar methods; (2) private prayer and meditation, when you pray and meditate alone, consciously putting yourself in the presence of your higher power or reflecting on your spiritual self; and (3) group worship, when you pray and meditate with others who share a similar spiritual philosophy.

A. "Do I believe I need to do this?" ❑ Yes ❑ Unsure ❑ No

B. "Obstacles that will prevent me from doing it are…"

____

____

C. "My plans for overcoming any obstacles are…"

____

____

D. "Will I put this on my recovery plan?" ❑ Yes ❑ Unsure ❑ No

Please explain:

____

____

7. **Morning and Evening Inventories:** People who avoid relapse and successfully recover, learn how to break free of automatic and unconscious self-defeating responses. They learn to live consciously each day, being aware of what they are doing and taking responsibility for what they do and its consequences. To stay consciously aware, they take time each morning to plan their day (a morning planning inventory) and they take time each evening to review their progress and problems (an evening review inventory). They discuss what they learn about themselves with other people involved in their recovery program.

A. "Do I believe that I need to do this?" ❑ Yes ❑ Unsure ❑ No

B. "Obstacles that will prevent me from doing it are..."

____

____

C. "My plans for overcoming any obstacles are..."

____

____

D. "Will I put this on my recovery plan?" ❑ Yes ❑ Unsure ❑ No

Please explain:

____

____

This exercise ends here.

Exercise 14—Part A: Your Initial Recovery Plan

Instructions: Think of a typical week and complete your recovery plan on the next page by:

A. entering the day and time of scheduled recovery activities (It helps to have two or three recovery activities scheduled each day.);

B. describing the recovery activity in the second column (A recovery activity is a specific thing you do at a scheduled time on a certain day. If you can't enter the activity onto a daily planner at a specific time, it is not a recovery activity);

C. describing the primary goal of that activity in preventing relapse.

Go to the next page to fill out your initial Recovery Plan.

Exercise 14—Part B: Your Initial Weekly Planner

Weekly Goals	Time	Sunday	Monday	Tuesday
	6:00 AM			
	7:00 AM			
	8:00 AM			
	9:00 AM			
	10:00 AM			
	11:00 AM			
	Noon			
	1:00 PM			
	2:00 PM			
	3:00 PM			
	4:00 PM			
	5:00 PM			
	6:00 PM			
	7:00 PM			
	8:00 PM			
	9:00 PM			
	10:00 PM			

Time	Wednesday	Thursday	Friday	Saturday
6:00 AM				
7:00 AM				
8:00 AM				
9:00 AM				
10:00 AM				
11:00 AM				
Noon				
1:00 PM				
2:00 PM				
3:00 PM				
4:00 PM				
5:00 PM				
6:00 PM				
7:00 PM				
8:00 PM				
9:00 PM				
10:00 PM				

Exercise 14—Part C: Testing Your Schedule of Recovery Activities

1. What is the primary warning sign you want your recovery program to help you identify and manage?

   ____

2. Look at your Weekly Planner. What's *the most-important* recovery activity that will help you manage this warning sign?

   ____

   A. How can you use this recovery activity to help you identify this relapse warning sign, should it occur?

   ____

   ____

   ____

   B. If you start to experience this warning sign again, how can you use this recovery activity to manage it?

   ____

   ____

   ____

3. Look at your Weekly Planner again. What's *the second-most-important* recovery activity that will help you manage this warning sign?

   ____

   A. How can you use this recovery activity to help you identify this relapse warning sign, should it occur?

   ____

   ____

   ____

   B. If you start to experience this warning sign again, how can you use this recovery activity to manage it?

   ____

   ____

   ____

4. Look at your Weekly Planner one last time. What's *the third-most-important* recovery activity that will help you manage this warning sign?

   ____

   A. How can you use this recovery activity to help you identify this relapse warning sign, should it occur?

   ____

   ____

   ____

B. If you start to experience this warning sign again, how can you use this recovery activity to manage it?

____

____

____

5. What other recovery activities might be more effective in helping you identify and manage this warning sign if it is activated?

____

____

____

____

Exercise 14—Part D: Your Final Recovery Plan

Your Final Weekly Planner

Weekly Goals	Time	Sunday	Monday	Tuesday
	6:00 AM			
	7:00 AM			
	8:00 AM			
	9:00 AM			
	10:00 AM			
	11:00 AM			
	Noon			
	1:00 PM			
	2:00 PM			
	3:00 PM			
	4:00 PM			
	5:00 PM			
	6:00 PM			
	7:00 PM			
	8:00 PM			
	9:00 PM			
	10:00 PM			

Time	Wednesday	Thursday	Friday	Saturday
6:00 AM				
7:00 AM				
8:00 AM				
9:00 AM				
10:00 AM				
11:00 AM				
Noon				
1:00 PM				
2:00 PM				
3:00 PM				
4:00 PM				
5:00 PM				
6:00 PM				
7:00 PM				
8:00 PM				
9:00 PM				
10:00 PM				

Exercise 14—Part E: Using a Daily Plan to Manage Your Critical-Warning Signs

Instructions: When learning to manage your critical-warning signs it is important to recognize the need for conscious daily planning. We often get ourselves into problem situations without consciously thinking about it. By using a daily plan, we can train ourselves to stay aware of relapse warning signs, and to make conscious decisions about how to manage them when they occur.

The most-effective way of working with a daily plan is to do a *Morning Planning Inventory* every morning and an *Evening Review Inventory* every night before bed. The morning planning inventory takes about fifteen minutes. It helps you plan your day, schedule your recovery activities, and stay aware of any warning signs you might experience. The evening review inventory takes about 15 minutes. It helps you review the activities of your day, evaluate how well you stuck to your recovery program, and notice if you experienced any relapse warning signs. It also gives you a chance to decide if you need help or support in dealing with what happened during the day.

The following forms are recommended for use during your morning and evening inventories. Make copies of these forms and use them every day.

Exercise 14—Part F: Using a Morning Planning Inventory

Instructions: Each morning, list your major goals for the day. In the first column, enter the recovery tasks you plan to complete today and then enter the other daily tasks you plan to complete. In column 2, assign a specific time during which you plan to complete each recovery task and other daily tasks.

Major Goals for Today: **Day:** ____________ **Date:** ______________________

❑ 1. ____

❑ 2. ____

❑ 3. ____

❑ 4. ____

❑ 5. ____

Recovery Tasks	Daily Time Plan
❑ 1.	6:00–7:00
❑ 2.	7:00–8:00
❑ 3.	8:00–9:00
❑ 4.	9:00–10:00
❑ 5.	10:00–11:00
Daily Tasks	11:00–12:00
❑ 1.	12:00–1:00
❑ 2.	1:00–2:00
❑ 3.	2:00–3:00
❑ 4.	3:00–4:00
❑ 5.	4:00–5:00
❑ 6.	5:00–6:00
❑ 7.	6:00–7:00
❑ 8.	7:00–8:00
❑ 9.	8:00–9:00
❑ 10.	9:00–10:00
❑ 11.	**Notes**
❑ 12.	
❑ 13.	
❑ 14.	
❑ 15.	

Exercise 14—Part G: Using an Evening Review Inventory

Instructions: Each evening before you go to bed review your morning plan and answer the questions below.

1. **Personal and Professional Progress**

   "Did I make progress today toward the accomplishment of my personal and professional goals?" ❑ Yes ❑ No ❑ Unsure

   How do I feel about that progress? ______________________________

   ____

2. **Personal and Professional Problems**

   "Did I make progress today toward solving my personal and professional problems?"

   ❑ Yes ❑ No ❑ Unsure

   "How do I feel about those problems?" ______________________________

   ____

3. **Relapse Warning Signs**

   "Did I experience any relapse warning signs?" ❑ Yes ❑ No ❑ Unsure

   If yes or unsure, briefly describe the situations you experienced: ______________

   ____

   ____

   "Did I think about or have an urge to use alcohol or other drugs in any of these situations?" ❑ Yes ❑ No ❑ Unsure

   "What did I do to manage those warning signs?" ______________________________

   ____

   ____

   "How do I feel about those warning sings and how I managed them?" ______________

   ____

   ____

4. **Decision about the Need for Outside Help**

   "Do I need to talk to someone about today's events?" ❑ Yes ❑ No ❑ Unsure

   "Do I need outside help with the high-risk situations that I experienced today?"

   ❑ Yes ❑ No ❑ Unsure

   "What feelings am I experiencing as I think about my need for outside help?"

   ____

   ____

The workbook exercises end here.

A Final Word from Terry and Steve

Your work in relapse prevention is never really over. There's a rule for personal growth and recovery—either we're growing, or we're dying. There is no standing still. We either commit ourselves each day to improving and refining our skills, or we become complacent and slowly move into the relapse cycle. We must make a conscious choice each day about which path we'll follow.

As you continue your recovery journey, remember that relapse prevention is about continuously identifying and managing future warning signs. The recovery process is like walking up a down escalator—if you stand still you go down. Also remember, there is no such thing as a hopeless person. There are only people who haven't learned how to develop an effective relapse prevention plan.

We wish you well on your personal journey of recovery! We're pleased and proud to have walked with you for a little while along the way. Thank you for permitting us to do so!

> Tomorrow Will Be New Again
> If We Have the Strength to Reach for Beauty
> And the Spirit to Pay Its Price!

—Terence T. Gorski & Stephen F. Grinstead

Notes

Notes

Notes

Notes

Warning Sign Identification Card—Side 1

Title: ________________________________

Description: I know I'm in trouble with my recovery when I…

____

____

Thought: When I experience this warning sign I tend to think…

____

____

Feeling: When I experience this warning sign I tend to feel…

____

____

Urge: When I experience this warning sign I have an urge to…

____

Action: When I experience this warning sign what I actually do is…

____

Reaction: I tend to invite others to become part of my problem by…

____

For reorders call: Herald Publishing House/Independence Press at 1-800-767-8181 or (816) 521-3015

THE CENAPS CORPORATION
TRAINING • CONSULTATION • RESEARCH

Please send me information on the Relapse Prevention Certification School.

Name ________________________________

Title ________________________________

Organization ________________________________

Work Address ________________________________

Work City/State/Zip ________________________________

Home Address ________________________________

Home City/State/Zip ________________________________

Work Phone ________________ Home/Cell Phone ________________

E-mail Address ________________________________

Warning Sign Identification Card—Side 1

Title: ________________________________

Description: I know I'm in trouble with my recovery when I…

____

____

Thought: When I experience this warning sign I tend to think…

____

____

Feeling: When I experience this warning sign I tend to feel…

____

____

Urge: When I experience this warning sign I have an urge to…

____

Action: When I experience this warning sign what I actually do is…

____

Reaction: I tend to invite others to become part of my problem by…

____

For reorders call: Herald Publishing House/Independence Press at 1-800-767-8181 or (816) 521-3015

Warning Sign Identification Card—Side 1

Title: ________________________________

Description: I know I'm in trouble with my recovery when I…

____

____

Thought: When I experience this warning sign I tend to think…

____

____

Feeling: When I experience this warning sign I tend to feel…

____

____

Urge: When I experience this warning sign I have an urge to…

____

Action: When I experience this warning sign what I actually do is…

____

Reaction: I tend to invite others to become part of my problem by…

____

For reorders call: Herald Publishing House/Independence Press at 1-800-767-8181 or (816) 521-3015

Warning Sign Identification Card—Side 2

Title: ____________________

Recovery Activities: The recovery activities I can use to manage this warning sign are…

____

____

Managing Thoughts: A new way of thinking that will help me manage this warning sign is…

____

____

Managing Feelings: A new way of managing my feelings is…

____

Managing Urges: A new way of managing my urges is…

____

Managing Actions: A new way of acting is…

____

Managing Reactions: A new way of inviting people to help me is…

____

Item #9780830913329

Warning Sign Identification Card—Side 2

Title: ____________________

Recovery Activities: The recovery activities I can use to manage this warning sign are…

____

____

Managing Thoughts: A new way of thinking that will help me manage this warning sign is…

____

____

Managing Feelings: A new way of managing my feelings is…

____

Managing Urges: A new way of managing my urges is…

____

Managing Actions: A new way of acting is…

____

Managing Reactions: A new way of inviting people to help me is…

____

© 2010 Terence T. Gorski CENAPS®

Item #9780830913329

Warning Sign Identification Card—Side 2

Title: ____________________

Recovery Activities: The recovery activities I can use to manage this warning sign are…

____

____

Managing Thoughts: A new way of thinking that will help me manage this warning sign is…

____

____

Managing Feelings: A new way of managing my feelings is…

____

Managing Urges: A new way of managing my urges is…

____

Managing Actions: A new way of acting is…

____

Managing Reactions: A new way of inviting people to help me is…

____

© 2010 Terence T. Gorski CENAPS®

Item #9780830913329

The Center for Applied Sciences
The CENAPS Corporation
13194 Spring Hill Drive
Spring Hill, FL 34609

Warning Sign Identification Card—Side 1

Title: ______________________

Description: I know I'm in trouble with my recovery when I…

____

____

Thought: When I experience this warning sign I tend to think…

____

____

Feeling: When I experience this warning sign I tend to feel…

____

____

Urge: When I experience this warning sign I have an urge to…

____

Action: When I experience this warning sign what I actually do is…

____

Reaction: I tend to invite others to become part of my problem by…

____

For reorders call: Herald Publishing House/Independence Press at 1-800-767-8181 or (816) 521-3015

Warning Sign Identification Card—Side 1

Title: ______________________

Description: I know I'm in trouble with my recovery when I…

____

____

Thought: When I experience this warning sign I tend to think…

____

____

Feeling: When I experience this warning sign I tend to feel…

____

____

Urge: When I experience this warning sign I have an urge to…

____

Action: When I experience this warning sign what I actually do is…

____

Reaction: I tend to invite others to become part of my problem by…

____

For reorders call: Herald Publishing House/Independence Press at 1-800-767-8181 or (816) 521-3015

Warning Sign Identification Card—Side 1

Title: ______________________

Description: I know I'm in trouble with my recovery when I…

____

____

Thought: When I experience this warning sign I tend to think…

____

____

Feeling: When I experience this warning sign I tend to feel…

____

____

Urge: When I experience this warning sign I have an urge to…

____

Action: When I experience this warning sign what I actually do is…

____

Reaction: I tend to invite others to become part of my problem by…

____

For reorders call: Herald Publishing House/Independence Press at 1-800-767-8181 or (816) 521-3015

Warning Sign Identification Card—Side 1

Title: ______________________

Description: I know I'm in trouble with my recovery when I…

____

____

Thought: When I experience this warning sign I tend to think…

____

____

Feeling: When I experience this warning sign I tend to feel…

____

____

Urge: When I experience this warning sign I have an urge to…

____

Action: When I experience this warning sign what I actually do is…

____

Reaction: I tend to invite others to become part of my problem by…

____

For reorders call: Herald Publishing House/Independence Press at 1-800-767-8181 or (816) 521-3015

Warning Sign Identification Card—Side 2

Title: ______________________

Recovery Activities: The recovery activities I can use to manage this warning sign are…

____

____

Managing Thoughts: A new way of thinking that will help me manage this warning sign is…

____

____

Managing Feelings: A new way of managing my feelings is…

____

Managing Urges: A new way of managing my urges is…

____

Managing Actions: A new way of acting is…

____

Managing Reactions: A new way of inviting people to help me is…

____

 Item #9780830913329

Warning Sign Identification Card—Side 2

Title: ______________________

Recovery Activities: The recovery activities I can use to manage this warning sign are…

____

____

Managing Thoughts: A new way of thinking that will help me manage this warning sign is…

____

____

Managing Feelings: A new way of managing my feelings is…

____

Managing Urges: A new way of managing my urges is…

____

Managing Actions: A new way of acting is…

____

Managing Reactions: A new way of inviting people to help me is…

____

© 2010 Terence T. Gorski CENAPS® Item #9780830913329

Warning Sign Identification Card—Side 2

Title: ______________________

Recovery Activities: The recovery activities I can use to manage this warning sign are…

____

____

Managing Thoughts: A new way of thinking that will help me manage this warning sign is…

____

____

Managing Feelings: A new way of managing my feelings is…

____

Managing Urges: A new way of managing my urges is…

____

Managing Actions: A new way of acting is…

____

Managing Reactions: A new way of inviting people to help me is…

____

© 2010 Terence T. Gorski CENAPS® Item #9780830913329

Warning Sign Identification Card—Side 2

Title: ______________________

Recovery Activities: The recovery activities I can use to manage this warning sign are…

____

____

Managing Thoughts: A new way of thinking that will help me manage this warning sign is…

____

____

Managing Feelings: A new way of managing my feelings is…

____

Managing Urges: A new way of managing my urges is…

____

Managing Actions: A new way of acting is…

____

Managing Reactions: A new way of inviting people to help me is…

____

© 2010 Terence T. Gorski CENAPS® Item #9780830913329

Warning Sign Identification Card—Side 1

Title: ____________________

Description: I know I'm in trouble with my recovery when I…

____

____

Thought: When I experience this warning sign I tend to think…

____

____

Feeling: When I experience this warning sign I tend to feel…

____

____

Urge: When I experience this warning sign I have an urge to…

____

Action: When I experience this warning sign what I actually do is…

____

Reaction: I tend to invite others to become part of my problem by…

____

For reorders call: Herald Publishing House/Independence Press at 1-800-767-8181 or (816) 521-3015

Warning Sign Identification Card—Side 1

Title: ____________________

Description: I know I'm in trouble with my recovery when I…

____

____

Thought: When I experience this warning sign I tend to think…

____

____

Feeling: When I experience this warning sign I tend to feel…

____

____

Urge: When I experience this warning sign I have an urge to…

____

Action: When I experience this warning sign what I actually do is…

____

Reaction: I tend to invite others to become part of my problem by…

____

For reorders call: Herald Publishing House/Independence Press at 1-800-767-8181 or (816) 521-3015

Warning Sign Identification Card—Side 1

Title: ____________________

Description: I know I'm in trouble with my recovery when I…

____

____

Thought: When I experience this warning sign I tend to think…

____

____

Feeling: When I experience this warning sign I tend to feel…

____

____

Urge: When I experience this warning sign I have an urge to…

____

Action: When I experience this warning sign what I actually do is…

____

Reaction: I tend to invite others to become part of my problem by…

____

For reorders call: Herald Publishing House/Independence Press at 1-800-767-8181 or (816) 521-3015

Warning Sign Identification Card—Side 1

Title: ____________________

Description: I know I'm in trouble with my recovery when I…

____

____

Thought: When I experience this warning sign I tend to think…

____

____

Feeling: When I experience this warning sign I tend to feel…

____

____

Urge: When I experience this warning sign I have an urge to…

____

Action: When I experience this warning sign what I actually do is…

____

Reaction: I tend to invite others to become part of my problem by…

____

For reorders call: Herald Publishing House/Independence Press at 1-800-767-8181 or (816) 521-3015

Warning Sign Identification Card—Side 2

Title: ______________________________

Recovery Activities: The recovery activities I can use to manage this warning sign are…

____

____

Managing Thoughts: A new way of thinking that will help me manage this warning sign is…

____

____

Managing Feelings: A new way of managing my feelings is…

____

Managing Urges: A new way of managing my urges is…

____

Managing Actions: A new way of acting is…

____

Managing Reactions: A new way of inviting people to help me is…

____

 Item #9780830913329

Warning Sign Identification Card—Side 2

Title: ______________________________

Recovery Activities: The recovery activities I can use to manage this warning sign are…

____

____

Managing Thoughts: A new way of thinking that will help me manage this warning sign is…

____

____

Managing Feelings: A new way of managing my feelings is…

____

Managing Urges: A new way of managing my urges is…

____

Managing Actions: A new way of acting is…

____

Managing Reactions: A new way of inviting people to help me is…

____

© 2010 Terence T. Gorski CENAPS® Item #9780830913329

Warning Sign Identification Card—Side 2

Title: ______________________________

Recovery Activities: The recovery activities I can use to manage this warning sign are…

____

____

Managing Thoughts: A new way of thinking that will help me manage this warning sign is…

____

____

Managing Feelings: A new way of managing my feelings is…

____

Managing Urges: A new way of managing my urges is…

____

Managing Actions: A new way of acting is…

____

Managing Reactions: A new way of inviting people to help me is…

____

© 2010 Terence T. Gorski CENAPS® Item #9780830913329

Warning Sign Identification Card—Side 2

Title: ______________________________

Recovery Activities: The recovery activities I can use to manage this warning sign are…

____

____

Managing Thoughts: A new way of thinking that will help me manage this warning sign is…

____

____

Managing Feelings: A new way of managing my feelings is…

____

Managing Urges: A new way of managing my urges is…

____

Managing Actions: A new way of acting is…

____

Managing Reactions: A new way of inviting people to help me is…

____

© 2010 Terence T. Gorski CENAPS® Item #9780830913329

Warning Sign Identification Card—Side 1

Title: ____________________

Description: I know I'm in trouble with my recovery when I...

____

____

Thought: When I experience this warning sign I tend to think...

____

____

Feeling: When I experience this warning sign I tend to feel...

____

____

Urge: When I experience this warning sign I have an urge to...

____

Action: When I experience this warning sign what I actually do is...

____

Reaction: I tend to invite others to become part of my problem by...

____

For reorders call: Herald Publishing House/Independence Press at 1-800-767-8181 or (816) 521-3015

Warning Sign Identification Card—Side 1

Title: ____________________

Description: I know I'm in trouble with my recovery when I...

____

____

Thought: When I experience this warning sign I tend to think...

____

____

Feeling: When I experience this warning sign I tend to feel...

____

____

Urge: When I experience this warning sign I have an urge to...

____

Action: When I experience this warning sign what I actually do is...

____

Reaction: I tend to invite others to become part of my problem by...

____

For reorders call: Herald Publishing House/Independence Press at 1-800-767-8181 or (816) 521-3015

Warning Sign Identification Card—Side 1

Title: ____________________

Description: I know I'm in trouble with my recovery when I...

____

____

Thought: When I experience this warning sign I tend to think...

____

____

Feeling: When I experience this warning sign I tend to feel...

____

____

Urge: When I experience this warning sign I have an urge to...

____

Action: When I experience this warning sign what I actually do is...

____

Reaction: I tend to invite others to become part of my problem by...

____

For reorders call: Herald Publishing House/Independence Press at 1-800-767-8181 or (816) 521-3015

Warning Sign Identification Card—Side 1

Title: ____________________

Description: I know I'm in trouble with my recovery when I...

____

____

Thought: When I experience this warning sign I tend to think...

____

____

Feeling: When I experience this warning sign I tend to feel...

____

____

Urge: When I experience this warning sign I have an urge to...

____

Action: When I experience this warning sign what I actually do is...

____

Reaction: I tend to invite others to become part of my problem by...

____

For reorders call: Herald Publishing House/Independence Press at 1-800-767-8181 or (816) 521-3015

Warning Sign Identification Card—Side 2

Title: ____________________

Recovery Activities: The recovery activities I can use to manage this warning sign are…

____

____

Managing Thoughts: A new way of thinking that will help me manage this warning sign is…

____

____

Managing Feelings: A new way of managing my feelings is…

____

Managing Urges: A new way of managing my urges is…

____

Managing Actions: A new way of acting is…

____

Managing Reactions: A new way of inviting people to help me is…

____

 Item #9780830913329

Warning Sign Identification Card—Side 2

Title: ____________________

Recovery Activities: The recovery activities I can use to manage this warning sign are…

____

____

Managing Thoughts: A new way of thinking that will help me manage this warning sign is…

____

____

Managing Feelings: A new way of managing my feelings is…

____

Managing Urges: A new way of managing my urges is…

____

Managing Actions: A new way of acting is…

____

Managing Reactions: A new way of inviting people to help me is…

____

© 2010 Terence T. Gorski CENAPS® Item #9780830913329

Warning Sign Identification Card—Side 2

Title: ____________________

Recovery Activities: The recovery activities I can use to manage this warning sign are…

____

____

Managing Thoughts: A new way of thinking that will help me manage this warning sign is…

____

____

Managing Feelings: A new way of managing my feelings is…

____

Managing Urges: A new way of managing my urges is…

____

Managing Actions: A new way of acting is…

____

Managing Reactions: A new way of inviting people to help me is…

____

© 2010 Terence T. Gorski CENAPS® Item #9780830913329

Warning Sign Identification Card—Side 2

Title: ____________________

Recovery Activities: The recovery activities I can use to manage this warning sign are…

____

____

Managing Thoughts: A new way of thinking that will help me manage this warning sign is…

____

____

Managing Feelings: A new way of managing my feelings is…

____

Managing Urges: A new way of managing my urges is…

____

Managing Actions: A new way of acting is…

____

Managing Reactions: A new way of inviting people to help me is…

____

© 2010 Terence T. Gorski CENAPS® Item #9780830913329

Warning Sign Identification Card—Side 1

Title: ______________________________

Description: I know I'm in trouble with my recovery when I...

____

____

Thought: When I experience this warning sign I tend to think...

____

____

Feeling: When I experience this warning sign I tend to feel...

____

____

Urge: When I experience this warning sign I have an urge to...

____

Action: When I experience this warning sign what I actually do is...

____

Reaction: I tend to invite others to become part of my problem by...

____

Warning Sign Identification Card—Side 1

Title: ______________________________

Description: I know I'm in trouble with my recovery when I...

____

____

Thought: When I experience this warning sign I tend to think...

____

____

Feeling: When I experience this warning sign I tend to feel...

____

____

Urge: When I experience this warning sign I have an urge to...

____

Action: When I experience this warning sign what I actually do is...

____

Reaction: I tend to invite others to become part of my problem by...

____

For reorders call: Herald Publishing House/Independence Press at 1-800-767-8181 or (816) 521-3015

Warning Sign Identification Card—Side 1

Title: ______________________________

Description: I know I'm in trouble with my recovery when I...

____

____

Thought: When I experience this warning sign I tend to think...

____

____

Feeling: When I experience this warning sign I tend to feel...

____

____

Urge: When I experience this warning sign I have an urge to...

____

Action: When I experience this warning sign what I actually do is...

____

Reaction: I tend to invite others to become part of my problem by...

____

For reorders call: Herald Publishing House/Independence Press at 1-800-767-8181 or (816) 521-3015

Warning Sign Identification Card—Side 1

Title: ______________________________

Description: I know I'm in trouble with my recovery when I...

____

____

Thought: When I experience this warning sign I tend to think...

____

____

Feeling: When I experience this warning sign I tend to feel...

____

____

Urge: When I experience this warning sign I have an urge to...

____

Action: When I experience this warning sign what I actually do is...

____

Reaction: I tend to invite others to become part of my problem by...

____

For reorders call: Herald Publishing House/Independence Press at 1-800-767-8181 or (816) 521-3015

Warning Sign Identification Card—Side 2

Title: ______________________________

Recovery Activities: The recovery activities I can use to manage this warning sign are…

____

____

Managing Thoughts: A new way of thinking that will help me manage this warning sign is…

____

____

Managing Feelings: A new way of managing my feelings is…

____

Managing Urges: A new way of managing my urges is…

____

Managing Actions: A new way of acting is…

____

Managing Reactions: A new way of inviting people to help me is…

____

 Item #9780830913329

Warning Sign Identification Card—Side 2

Title: ______________________________

Recovery Activities: The recovery activities I can use to manage this warning sign are…

____

____

Managing Thoughts: A new way of thinking that will help me manage this warning sign is…

____

____

Managing Feelings: A new way of managing my feelings is…

____

Managing Urges: A new way of managing my urges is…

____

Managing Actions: A new way of acting is…

____

Managing Reactions: A new way of inviting people to help me is…

____

© 2010 Terence T. Gorski CENAPS® Item #9780830913329

Warning Sign Identification Card—Side 2

Title: ______________________________

Recovery Activities: The recovery activities I can use to manage this warning sign are…

____

____

Managing Thoughts: A new way of thinking that will help me manage this warning sign is…

____

____

Managing Feelings: A new way of managing my feelings is…

____

Managing Urges: A new way of managing my urges is…

____

Managing Actions: A new way of acting is…

____

Managing Reactions: A new way of inviting people to help me is…

____

© 2010 Terence T. Gorski CENAPS® Item #9780830913329

Warning Sign Identification Card—Side 2

Title: ______________________________

Recovery Activities: The recovery activities I can use to manage this warning sign are…

____

____

Managing Thoughts: A new way of thinking that will help me manage this warning sign is…

____

____

Managing Feelings: A new way of managing my feelings is…

____

Managing Urges: A new way of managing my urges is…

____

Managing Actions: A new way of acting is…

____

Managing Reactions: A new way of inviting people to help me is…

____

© 2010 Terence T. Gorski CENAPS® Item #9780830913329

Warning Sign Identification Card—Side 1

Title: ______________________________

Description: I know I'm in trouble with my recovery when I…

____

____

Thought: When I experience this warning sign I tend to think…

____

____

Feeling: When I experience this warning sign I tend to feel…

____

____

Urge: When I experience this warning sign I have an urge to…

____

Action: When I experience this warning sign what I actually do is…

____

Reaction: I tend to invite others to become part of my problem by…

____

For reorders call: Herald Publishing House/Independence Press at 1-800-767-8181 or (816) 521-3015

Warning Sign Identification Card—Side 1

Title: ______________________________

Description: I know I'm in trouble with my recovery when I…

____

____

Thought: When I experience this warning sign I tend to think…

____

____

Feeling: When I experience this warning sign I tend to feel…

____

____

Urge: When I experience this warning sign I have an urge to…

____

Action: When I experience this warning sign what I actually do is…

____

Reaction: I tend to invite others to become part of my problem by…

____

For reorders call: Herald Publishing House/Independence Press at 1-800-767-8181 or (816) 521-3015

Warning Sign Identification Card—Side 1

Title: ______________________________

Description: I know I'm in trouble with my recovery when I…

____

____

Thought: When I experience this warning sign I tend to think…

____

____

Feeling: When I experience this warning sign I tend to feel…

____

____

Urge: When I experience this warning sign I have an urge to…

____

Action: When I experience this warning sign what I actually do is…

____

Reaction: I tend to invite others to become part of my problem by…

____

For reorders call: Herald Publishing House/Independence Press at 1-800-767-8181 or (816) 521-3015

Warning Sign Identification Card—Side 1

Title: ______________________________

Description: I know I'm in trouble with my recovery when I…

____

____

Thought: When I experience this warning sign I tend to think…

____

____

Feeling: When I experience this warning sign I tend to feel…

____

____

Urge: When I experience this warning sign I have an urge to…

____

Action: When I experience this warning sign what I actually do is…

____

Reaction: I tend to invite others to become part of my problem by…

____

For reorders call: Herald Publishing House/Independence Press at 1-800-767-8181 or (816) 521-3015

Warning Sign Identification Card—Side 2

Title: ______________________________

Recovery Activities: The recovery activities I can use to manage this warning sign are…

____

____

Managing Thoughts: A new way of thinking that will help me manage this warning sign is…

____

____

Managing Feelings: A new way of managing my feelings is…

____

Managing Urges: A new way of managing my urges is…

____

Managing Actions: A new way of acting is…

____

Managing Reactions: A new way of inviting people to help me is…

____

 Item #9780830913329

Warning Sign Identification Card—Side 2

Title: ______________________________

Recovery Activities: The recovery activities I can use to manage this warning sign are…

____

____

Managing Thoughts: A new way of thinking that will help me manage this warning sign is…

____

____

Managing Feelings: A new way of managing my feelings is…

____

Managing Urges: A new way of managing my urges is…

____

Managing Actions: A new way of acting is…

____

Managing Reactions: A new way of inviting people to help me is…

____

© 2010 Terence T. Gorski CENAPS® Item #9780830913329

Warning Sign Identification Card—Side 2

Title: ______________________________

Recovery Activities: The recovery activities I can use to manage this warning sign are…

____

____

Managing Thoughts: A new way of thinking that will help me manage this warning sign is…

____

____

Managing Feelings: A new way of managing my feelings is…

____

Managing Urges: A new way of managing my urges is…

____

Managing Actions: A new way of acting is…

____

Managing Reactions: A new way of inviting people to help me is…

____

© 2010 Terence T. Gorski CENAPS® Item #9780830913329

Warning Sign Identification Card—Side 2

Title: ______________________________

Recovery Activities: The recovery activities I can use to manage this warning sign are…

____

____

Managing Thoughts: A new way of thinking that will help me manage this warning sign is…

____

____

Managing Feelings: A new way of managing my feelings is…

____

Managing Urges: A new way of managing my urges is…

____

Managing Actions: A new way of acting is…

____

Managing Reactions: A new way of inviting people to help me is…

____

© 2010 Terence T. Gorski CENAPS® Item #9780830913329

Warning Sign Identification Card—Side 1

Title: ____________________

Description: I know I'm in trouble with my recovery when I...

____

____

Thought: When I experience this warning sign I tend to think...

____

____

Feeling: When I experience this warning sign I tend to feel...

____

____

Urge: When I experience this warning sign I have an urge to...

____

Action: When I experience this warning sign what I actually do is...

____

Reaction: I tend to invite others to become part of my problem by...

____

For reorders call: Herald Publishing House/Independence Press at 1-800-767-8181 or (816) 521-3015

Warning Sign Identification Card—Side 1

Title: ____________________

Description: I know I'm in trouble with my recovery when I...

____

____

Thought: When I experience this warning sign I tend to think...

____

____

Feeling: When I experience this warning sign I tend to feel...

____

____

Urge: When I experience this warning sign I have an urge to...

____

Action: When I experience this warning sign what I actually do is...

____

Reaction: I tend to invite others to become part of my problem by...

____

For reorders call: Herald Publishing House/Independence Press at 1-800-767-8181 or (816) 521-3015

Warning Sign Identification Card—Side 1

Title: ____________________

Description: I know I'm in trouble with my recovery when I...

____

____

Thought: When I experience this warning sign I tend to think...

____

____

Feeling: When I experience this warning sign I tend to feel...

____

____

Urge: When I experience this warning sign I have an urge to...

____

Action: When I experience this warning sign what I actually do is...

____

Reaction: I tend to invite others to become part of my problem by...

____

For reorders call: Herald Publishing House/Independence Press at 1-800-767-8181 or (816) 521-3015

Warning Sign Identification Card—Side 1

Title: ____________________

Description: I know I'm in trouble with my recovery when I...

____

____

Thought: When I experience this warning sign I tend to think...

____

____

Feeling: When I experience this warning sign I tend to feel...

____

____

Urge: When I experience this warning sign I have an urge to...

____

Action: When I experience this warning sign what I actually do is...

____

Reaction: I tend to invite others to become part of my problem by...

____

For reorders call: Herald Publishing House/Independence Press at 1-800-767-8181 or (816) 521-3015

Warning Sign Identification Card—Side 2

Title: ____________________

Recovery Activities: The recovery activities I can use to manage this warning sign are…

____

____

Managing Thoughts: A new way of thinking that will help me manage this warning sign is…

____

____

Managing Feelings: A new way of managing my feelings is…

____

Managing Urges: A new way of managing my urges is…

____

Managing Actions: A new way of acting is…

____

Managing Reactions: A new way of inviting people to help me is…

____

 Item #9780830913329

Warning Sign Identification Card—Side 2

Title: ____________________

Recovery Activities: The recovery activities I can use to manage this warning sign are…

____

____

Managing Thoughts: A new way of thinking that will help me manage this warning sign is…

____

____

Managing Feelings: A new way of managing my feelings is…

____

Managing Urges: A new way of managing my urges is…

____

Managing Actions: A new way of acting is…

____

Managing Reactions: A new way of inviting people to help me is…

____

© 2010 Terence T. Gorski CENAPS® Item #9780830913329

Warning Sign Identification Card—Side 2

Title: ____________________

Recovery Activities: The recovery activities I can use to manage this warning sign are…

____

____

Managing Thoughts: A new way of thinking that will help me manage this warning sign is…

____

____

Managing Feelings: A new way of managing my feelings is…

____

Managing Urges: A new way of managing my urges is…

____

Managing Actions: A new way of acting is…

____

Managing Reactions: A new way of inviting people to help me is…

____

© 2010 Terence T. Gorski CENAPS® Item #9780830913329

Warning Sign Identification Card—Side 2

Title: ____________________

Recovery Activities: The recovery activities I can use to manage this warning sign are…

____

____

Managing Thoughts: A new way of thinking that will help me manage this warning sign is…

____

____

Managing Feelings: A new way of managing my feelings is…

____

Managing Urges: A new way of managing my urges is…

____

Managing Actions: A new way of acting is…

____

Managing Reactions: A new way of inviting people to help me is…

____

© 2010 Terence T. Gorski CENAPS® Item #9780830913329

Warning Sign Identification Card—Side 1

Title: ____________________

Description: I know I'm in trouble with my recovery when I…

____

____

Thought: When I experience this warning sign I tend to think…

____

____

Feeling: When I experience this warning sign I tend to feel…

____

____

Urge: When I experience this warning sign I have an urge to…

____

Action: When I experience this warning sign what I actually do is…

____

Reaction: I tend to invite others to become part of my problem by…

____

For reorders call: Herald Publishing House/Independence Press at 1-800-767-8181 or (816) 521-3015

Warning Sign Identification Card—Side 1

Title: ____________________

Description: I know I'm in trouble with my recovery when I…

____

____

Thought: When I experience this warning sign I tend to think…

____

____

Feeling: When I experience this warning sign I tend to feel…

____

____

Urge: When I experience this warning sign I have an urge to…

____

Action: When I experience this warning sign what I actually do is…

____

Reaction: I tend to invite others to become part of my problem by…

____

For reorders call: Herald Publishing House/Independence Press at 1-800-767-8181 or (816) 521-3015

Warning Sign Identification Card—Side 1

Title: ____________________

Description: I know I'm in trouble with my recovery when I…

____

____

Thought: When I experience this warning sign I tend to think…

____

____

Feeling: When I experience this warning sign I tend to feel…

____

____

Urge: When I experience this warning sign I have an urge to…

____

Action: When I experience this warning sign what I actually do is…

____

Reaction: I tend to invite others to become part of my problem by…

____

For reorders call: Herald Publishing House/Independence Press at 1-800-767-8181 or (816) 521-3015

Warning Sign Identification Card—Side 1

Title: ____________________

Description: I know I'm in trouble with my recovery when I…

____

____

Thought: When I experience this warning sign I tend to think…

____

____

Feeling: When I experience this warning sign I tend to feel…

____

____

Urge: When I experience this warning sign I have an urge to…

____

Action: When I experience this warning sign what I actually do is…

____

Reaction: I tend to invite others to become part of my problem by…

____

For reorders call: Herald Publishing House/Independence Press at 1-800-767-8181 or (816) 521-3015

Warning Sign Identification Card—Side 2

Title: ______________________________

Recovery Activities: The recovery activities I can use to manage this warning sign are…

____

____

Managing Thoughts: A new way of thinking that will help me manage this warning sign is…

____

____

Managing Feelings: A new way of managing my feelings is…

____

Managing Urges: A new way of managing my urges is…

____

Managing Actions: A new way of acting is…

____

Managing Reactions: A new way of inviting people to help me is…

____

 Item #9780830913329

Warning Sign Identification Card—Side 2

Title: ______________________________

Recovery Activities: The recovery activities I can use to manage this warning sign are…

____

____

Managing Thoughts: A new way of thinking that will help me manage this warning sign is…

____

____

Managing Feelings: A new way of managing my feelings is…

____

Managing Urges: A new way of managing my urges is…

____

Managing Actions: A new way of acting is…

____

Managing Reactions: A new way of inviting people to help me is…

____

© 2010 Terence T. Gorski CENAPS® Item #9780830913329

Warning Sign Identification Card—Side 2

Title: ______________________________

Recovery Activities: The recovery activities I can use to manage this warning sign are…

____

____

Managing Thoughts: A new way of thinking that will help me manage this warning sign is…

____

____

Managing Feelings: A new way of managing my feelings is…

____

Managing Urges: A new way of managing my urges is…

____

Managing Actions: A new way of acting is…

____

Managing Reactions: A new way of inviting people to help me is…

____

© 2010 Terence T. Gorski CENAPS® Item #9780830913329

Warning Sign Identification Card—Side 2

Title: ______________________________

Recovery Activities: The recovery activities I can use to manage this warning sign are…

____

____

Managing Thoughts: A new way of thinking that will help me manage this warning sign is…

____

____

Managing Feelings: A new way of managing my feelings is…

____

Managing Urges: A new way of managing my urges is…

____

Managing Actions: A new way of acting is…

____

Managing Reactions: A new way of inviting people to help me is…

____

© 2010 Terence T. Gorski CENAPS® Item #9780830913329

Warning Sign Identification Card—Side 1

Title: ______

Description: I know I'm in trouble with my recovery when I…

Thought: When I experience this warning sign I tend to think…

Feeling: When I experience this warning sign I tend to feel…

Urge: When I experience this warning sign I have an urge to…

Action: When I experience this warning sign what I actually do is…

Reaction: I tend to invite others to become part of my problem by…

For reorders call: Herald Publishing House/Independence Press at 1-800-767-8181 or (816) 521-3015

Warning Sign Identification Card—Side 1

Title: ______

Description: I know I'm in trouble with my recovery when I…

Thought: When I experience this warning sign I tend to think…

Feeling: When I experience this warning sign I tend to feel…

Urge: When I experience this warning sign I have an urge to…

Action: When I experience this warning sign what I actually do is…

Reaction: I tend to invite others to become part of my problem by…

For reorders call: Herald Publishing House/Independence Press at 1-800-767-8181 or (816) 521-3015

Warning Sign Identification Card—Side 1

Title: ______

Description: I know I'm in trouble with my recovery when I…

Thought: When I experience this warning sign I tend to think…

Feeling: When I experience this warning sign I tend to feel…

Urge: When I experience this warning sign I have an urge to…

Action: When I experience this warning sign what I actually do is…

Reaction: I tend to invite others to become part of my problem by…

For reorders call: Herald Publishing House/Independence Press at 1-800-767-8181 or (816) 521-3015

Warning Sign Identification Card—Side 1

Title: ______

Description: I know I'm in trouble with my recovery when I…

Thought: When I experience this warning sign I tend to think…

Feeling: When I experience this warning sign I tend to feel…

Urge: When I experience this warning sign I have an urge to…

Action: When I experience this warning sign what I actually do is…

Reaction: I tend to invite others to become part of my problem by…

For reorders call: Herald Publishing House/Independence Press at 1-800-767-8181 or (816) 521-3015

Warning Sign Identification Card—Side 2

Title: ____________________________

Recovery Activities: The recovery activities I can use to manage this warning sign are…

____

____

Managing Thoughts: A new way of thinking that will help me manage this warning sign is…

____

____

Managing Feelings: A new way of managing my feelings is…

____

Managing Urges: A new way of managing my urges is…

____

Managing Actions: A new way of acting is…

____

Managing Reactions: A new way of inviting people to help me is…

____

 Item #9780830913329

Warning Sign Identification Card—Side 2

Title: ____________________________

Recovery Activities: The recovery activities I can use to manage this warning sign are…

____

____

Managing Thoughts: A new way of thinking that will help me manage this warning sign is…

____

____

Managing Feelings: A new way of managing my feelings is…

____

Managing Urges: A new way of managing my urges is…

____

Managing Actions: A new way of acting is…

____

Managing Reactions: A new way of inviting people to help me is…

____

© 2010 Terence T. Gorski CENAPS® Item #9780830913329

Warning Sign Identification Card—Side 2

Title: ____________________________

Recovery Activities: The recovery activities I can use to manage this warning sign are…

____

____

Managing Thoughts: A new way of thinking that will help me manage this warning sign is…

____

____

Managing Feelings: A new way of managing my feelings is…

____

Managing Urges: A new way of managing my urges is…

____

Managing Actions: A new way of acting is…

____

Managing Reactions: A new way of inviting people to help me is…

____

© 2010 Terence T. Gorski CENAPS® Item #9780830913329

Warning Sign Identification Card—Side 2

Title: ____________________________

Recovery Activities: The recovery activities I can use to manage this warning sign are…

____

____

Managing Thoughts: A new way of thinking that will help me manage this warning sign is…

____

____

Managing Feelings: A new way of managing my feelings is…

____

Managing Urges: A new way of managing my urges is…

____

Managing Actions: A new way of acting is…

____

Managing Reactions: A new way of inviting people to help me is…

____

© 2010 Terence T. Gorski CENAPS® Item #9780830913329

Warning Sign Identification Card—Side 1

Title: ____________________

Description: I know I'm in trouble with my recovery when I...

____

____

Thought: When I experience this warning sign I tend to think...

____

____

Feeling: When I experience this warning sign I tend to feel...

____

____

Urge: When I experience this warning sign I have an urge to...

____

Action: When I experience this warning sign what I actually do is...

____

Reaction: I tend to invite others to become part of my problem by...

____

For reorders call: Herald Publishing House/Independence Press at 1-800-767-8181 or (816) 521-3015

Warning Sign Identification Card—Side 1

Title: ____________________

Description: I know I'm in trouble with my recovery when I...

____

____

Thought: When I experience this warning sign I tend to think...

____

____

Feeling: When I experience this warning sign I tend to feel...

____

____

Urge: When I experience this warning sign I have an urge to...

____

Action: When I experience this warning sign what I actually do is...

____

Reaction: I tend to invite others to become part of my problem by...

____

For reorders call: Herald Publishing House/Independence Press at 1-800-767-8181 or (816) 521-3015

Warning Sign Identification Card—Side 1

Title: ____________________

Description: I know I'm in trouble with my recovery when I...

____

____

Thought: When I experience this warning sign I tend to think...

____

____

Feeling: When I experience this warning sign I tend to feel...

____

____

Urge: When I experience this warning sign I have an urge to...

____

Action: When I experience this warning sign what I actually do is...

____

Reaction: I tend to invite others to become part of my problem by...

____

For reorders call: Herald Publishing House/Independence Press at 1-800-767-8181 or (816) 521-3015

Warning Sign Identification Card—Side 1

Title: ____________________

Description: I know I'm in trouble with my recovery when I...

____

____

Thought: When I experience this warning sign I tend to think...

____

____

Feeling: When I experience this warning sign I tend to feel...

____

____

Urge: When I experience this warning sign I have an urge to...

____

Action: When I experience this warning sign what I actually do is...

____

Reaction: I tend to invite others to become part of my problem by...

____

For reorders call: Herald Publishing House/Independence Press at 1-800-767-8181 or (816) 521-3015

Warning Sign Identification Card—Side 2

Title: ______________________________

Recovery Activities: The recovery activities I can use to manage this warning sign are…

Managing Thoughts: A new way of thinking that will help me manage this warning sign is…

Managing Feelings: A new way of managing my feelings is…

Managing Urges: A new way of managing my urges is…

Managing Actions: A new way of acting is…

Managing Reactions: A new way of inviting people to help me is…

Item #9780830913329

Warning Sign Identification Card—Side 2

Title: ______________________________

Recovery Activities: The recovery activities I can use to manage this warning sign are…

Managing Thoughts: A new way of thinking that will help me manage this warning sign is…

Managing Feelings: A new way of managing my feelings is…

Managing Urges: A new way of managing my urges is…

Managing Actions: A new way of acting is…

Managing Reactions: A new way of inviting people to help me is…

© 2010 Terence T. Gorski CENAPS®

Item #9780830913329

Warning Sign Identification Card—Side 2

Title: ______________________________

Recovery Activities: The recovery activities I can use to manage this warning sign are…

Managing Thoughts: A new way of thinking that will help me manage this warning sign is…

Managing Feelings: A new way of managing my feelings is…

Managing Urges: A new way of managing my urges is…

Managing Actions: A new way of acting is…

Managing Reactions: A new way of inviting people to help me is…

© 2010 Terence T. Gorski CENAPS®

Item #9780830913329

Warning Sign Identification Card—Side 2

Title: ______________________________

Recovery Activities: The recovery activities I can use to manage this warning sign are…

Managing Thoughts: A new way of thinking that will help me manage this warning sign is…

Managing Feelings: A new way of managing my feelings is…

Managing Urges: A new way of managing my urges is…

Managing Actions: A new way of acting is…

Managing Reactions: A new way of inviting people to help me is…

© 2010 Terence T. Gorski CENAPS®

Item #9780830913329